Thomas A. Edison

Lamps for a Brighter America

A HISTORY OF THE GENERAL ELECTRIC LAMP BUSINESS

Paul W. Keating

First Edition

McGRAW-HILL BOOK COMPANY, INC.   1954

New York   Toronto   London

Acknowledgments

D URING 20 YEARS of writing and editorial work, the writer of this book has come to know rather well the men and women of the major lamp companies. It is his opinion that they are truly exceptional in ability and in their regard for the public interest as related to their work. It has therefore been a genuine pleasure to develop this history of the General Electric lamp business.

Like the activities of the G-E Lamp Division, this was more a group project than the work of one individual.

Many people contributed advice and counsel, facts and figures. Others have reviewed manuscript and proofs, making many helpful suggestions. We have had admirable assistance from stenographic, clerical, and art-work specialists.

This book helps to celebrate Light's Diamond Jubilee—75 years of electric-lighting progress. It would be difficult to assess comparatively the contributions of individuals (in the General Electric Company and elsewhere) in making this history possible. Therefore the following alphabetical listing merely attempts to include those who have materially aided the writer:

Oscar P. Anderson, Quincy D. Baldwin, Willard C. Brown, Robert P. Burrows, Clarence L. Davis, Benjamin F. Fisher, Max N. Fuldauer, Walter J. Geiger, Newell T. Gordon, Harold H. Green, Laurence A. Hawkins, Victor E. Hollenfer, Dale C. Hughes, Ralph H. Humbert, Gordon D. Hurd, George E. Inman, Vernet C. Kauffman, Katherine B. Keating, James M. Ketch,

Col. Jay A. J. Lee, John C. Lloyd, Herbert H. Magdsick, Leslie P. Moyer, John F. McClenahen, Donald L. Millham, James V. Nardi, Carl L. Olson, Philip J. Pritchard, Kenneth G. Reider, Neil B. Reynolds, William H. Robinson, Jr., Rachel E. Sayers, Richard N. Thayer.

Many excellent books and periodicals devoted to a record of the lamp business have been utilized in the research for the book. This work by earlier writers (too many to be listed here) has been of inestimable value. At the same time, much of the information has come from original sources never before available.

The writer especially wishes to make clear the following points:

1. It is almost impossible, in a business history of this character, to adjudge—or even to state—the countless individual achievements in the progress of the business. This is due to (*a*) failing memories, (*b*) the group character of many contributions, (*c*) dislike for personal publicity or recognition, and (*d*) limitations of space.

2. As a result, some individuals may be slightly overpraised, others may be unjustly neglected. The writer feels that this insoluble problem is important, but not all-important. The main criterion is this: Have we given a reasonably true picture of 75 years in G-E lamp history? We hope that we have done so.

3. It would be most surprising if there were no minor errors of fact or emphasis in these pages. The checking has been careful and extensive. Any and all errors that may have occurred are attributable only to the undersigned.

Paul W. Keating

Contents

vii

Introduction

I N YOUR DAILY life, lamp bulbs and electric lighting are so familiar that you take them for granted. You flick a switch, and there is light—as you need it, when and where you want it.

What's interesting about a lamp bulb? It simply fits into a socket —in your home, your school, or your place of business. It gives you light just as other bulbs have done before in the same socket. There is nothing new about this. You've seen lamp bulbs for years, probably all your life.

Yet there is a significant story behind these lamps—a dramatic story of human effort, of many men's dreams and hopes. It is a record of research, scientific progress, manufacturing skill, and management foresight.

This book tells that story, for this is a history of the highlights in the development of the General Electric lamp business.

The heart of modern man-made lighting is the electric lamp: the incandescent bulb or the fluorescent tube, glowing with soft, useful light. And the lamp business, as described here, deals with these and many other types of basic light sources.

Most people think of the word "lamp" as meaning a floor lamp or table lamp such as you have in your home. In the trade these are called "portable lamps." That term distinguishes them from lighting fixtures permanently attached to the ceilings or walls. Fixtures and portable lamps are, in effect, "holders" for the light source. But in this book the word "lamp" is used as the electrical engineer uses it, meaning the *bulb* or the *tube* that converts electrical energy into light.

1

The first commercially practical incandescent lamp bulb was a product of the inventive genius of Thomas A. Edison. Today it seems crude indeed by comparison with the millions of marvelously precise bulbs and tubes that flow out of the General Electric lamp factories every week. But in 1879 it represented an extraordinary achievement, greeted by breathless headlines and a full-page story in the New York *Herald*.

Edison's was not the first incandescent lamp, but it was the first that could be successfully used to establish a new lighting industry. The Edison lamp and its successors triumphed over both gas illumination and electric-arc lighting in the competition for lighting supremacy.

Man instinctively loves light and usually dislikes darkness. Without this fact, the modern lighting industry would probably never have existed. As it is, the makers of lamps have fostered that love of light and have served it diligently through the years. Many scientists, engineers, and skilled workmen have improved the lamps tremendously since Edison's victory in the laboratory. They have developed many entirely new types of lamps. Their contributions, while perhaps less widely known than Edison's, are certainly no less important to human welfare. Many such developments will be reported in these pages.

The record of man's search for ever-better illumination has fascinated countless men of science. Edison was influenced by it, and so were the other experimenters who were working in this field in the late nineteenth century. Therefore this chronicle begins with some of the notable steps of the past in the long history of lighting progress.

PART ONE

In Search of Better Lighting

CHAPTER I

From Fire to Filaments

LAMP BULBS as we know them today are precision instruments, yet they sell for only a few cents. The filament—the length of fine wire that glows with incandescence—best illustrates the accuracy with which good lamps are made. The tungsten filament of a 60-watt bulb operates at a temperature twice as high as that of molten steel in a blast furnace. Asbestos or fire brick would melt like wax at such a heat. Yet the tiny filament wire in the lamp measures less than $\frac{2}{1,000}$ inch in diameter—finer than a human hair.

A lamp manufacturer such as the General Electric Company cannot permit the filaments in such lamps to vary even 1 per cent from the specified size. If a filament is that much smaller in even a minute part of its length, the life of the lamp may be reduced by one-fourth.

Of course there are many smaller filaments than those in the 60-watt bulb. For instance, in a 6-watt 120-volt lamp, the filament is about one-sixth the diameter of a human hair. It would take 2,130 such filaments laid side by side to measure 1 inch.

The filament is only one of many precision parts in a lamp bulb. Yet General Electric produces and sells millions of lamps per day at low cost. Today's lamp produces nearly 80 per cent more light than the comparable bulbs of 1907 that sold for as much as $1.75.

It has taken 75 years of scientific research and manufacturing progress to bring these products to their present degree of perfection. Naturally the larger lamps and various specialized types cost more than the most widely used sizes and types, but all are inexpensive in terms of lighting advantages. Today we take them for granted—incandescent bulbs, fluorescent tubes, spotlights, photo-flash lamps, sealed-beam lamps, and a hundred other kinds in daily use. Yet they have changed the lives of countless millions of people —by making life richer, easier, and more satisfying.

USING FLAME FOR LIGHT

Against the backdrop of thousands of years in the history of mankind, electric light appears as a recent addition to the scene. Until about 1802 even the possibility of such lighting remained beyond imagination. Then another 77 years passed before the glow of Edison's lamp bulb made it possible to move ahead toward modern lighting.

Through the earlier years of recorded time, the only widely used sources of man-made light were *flame sources*. The first of these was the campfire of the cave man, dozens of centuries ago. The fire staved off the attacks of wild animals. Beyond that, it could hardly be called very useful as a medium of lighting. But then the cave man had little further need for light after sundown.

In later times, when man moved indoors, the flame sources of light included many kinds of torches, candles, and oil lamps. Candles served our forefathers as their principal source of light until the early part of the nineteenth century. At that time experimenters in Great Britain and France devised systems of using gas for illumination. By 1820 similar methods had been adopted in some of the large cities in the United States.

Progress in making and selling this new illuminant was slow until about 1850. Even after gas lighting had expanded greatly (1850–1880), oil lamps and sometimes candles continued in use for many years in rural and small-town areas. This remained true until well into the era of electricity.

Many people living today remember childhood evenings spent reading or studying by the flickering, pale light of kerosene lamps. An abundance of "fuss and muss" accompanied the use of this lighting, just as in using candles. The fragile glass chimneys had to be washed frequently; wicks had to be trimmed and the lamps re-filled with fuel. The danger of fire was ever present.

Eventually, gas companies took over most of the lighting market. Because it came from a flame source, the light still flickered. There were serious fire and health hazards. The method was still an inefficient one, low in light output. But it was better than the oil lamp and the candle. So gas illumination remained the standard system until the emergence of practical electric lighting. By 1880 there were more than 500 illuminating-gas companies in the United States.

The greatest improvement in gas lighting—the Welsbach mantle—occurred after Edison's electric-lamp invention. Even so, the last and best flame source of light could not compete successfully with electricity in the long run. The competitive struggle between gas light and the electric lamp lasted about 30 years. By 1910, however, electricity was clearly supreme in the lighting field.

EARLY ELECTRIC LIGHTING

The English chemist, Humphry Davy, was the first noted experimenter in the development of electric light. From 1802 to about 1810 Davy made several basic discoveries. In the last two years of this period he demonstrated an electric-arc light operated by a battery.

Other experiments in electricity, largely European, followed in the years from 1830 to 1870. In 1831 Michael Faraday, the British scientist, and Joseph Henry, an American, discovered the principle of electromagnetic induction. The two men worked independently but arrived at similar conclusions. Their findings greatly stimulated the development of the dynamo as a means of supplying current. This in turn resulted in progress in arc lighting.

Davy's work led also to the first crude incandescent lamps. The man credited with the first such lamp was an Englishman named De la Rue, who used a coil of platinum wire as a "burner" in a length of glass tubing. This was in 1820.

Others who built lamps included Grove (1840), De Moleyns

(1841), Starr (1845), Staite (1848), Shepard (1850), and Roberts (1852). Starr and Shepard were Americans, the others British. The first patent for an incandescent lamp, issued in England, was granted to De Moleyns. The lamps devised by these pioneers were ingenious. They used platinum, carbon rods, graphite, and charcoal as burners, and a variety of enclosing devices. But none of the lamps could be utilized practically for a lighting system. They were interesting creations of the laboratory and workshop—nothing more.

The first lamps used to light a room in a home, purely as a demonstration of the strange wonders of electricity, came from the hands of Moses G. Farmer in 1859. Farmer, a New Englander, invented many electrical devices. The lamp demonstration took place in his home in Salem, Mass. The contemporary records do not state whether the good citizens of Salem regarded the dimly burning lamps as examples of witchcraft. For their time, however, the lamps must have been considered miraculous. Today Farmer's contrivance would hardly be recognized as a lamp. It consisted of a strip of sheet platinum narrowed at the ends and fitted into a pair of clamps. Operated in the open air, the burner became incandescent when powered by batteries.

Joseph W. Swan, who later became a leading lamp manufacturer in England, developed a lamp in 1860. However, the vacuum he created in a bell jar surrounding the burner was destroyed by air leaks and the lamp soon failed to operate. The burner Swan used at this time was carbonized paper.

Several Russian scientists also created incandescent lamps during the years 1872–1876. The most prominent among them was Alexander Lodyguine.

NEARING THE GOAL

The years from 1877 to 1880 were a time of intensive experimentation in the invention of incandescent lamps. Guided by the earlier efforts described above, the work in this period was spurred by three main lines of electrical research: the development of arc lighting; perfection of the dynamo; and improvement of the vacuum pump.

Arc lamps consisted basically of two electrodes, usually made of carbon, that were separated from each other by a short air space or gap. Electric current applied to one of the electrodes flowed to and through the other electrode, striking an arc across the gap. The glowing arc and the adjacent incandescent ends of the electrodes provided light.

Extensive European development of arc lighting, which had occurred from 1870 to 1877, was followed by American improvements. In 1877 Charles F. Brush of Cleveland, Ohio, the holder of numerous patents in telegraphy, invented a good arc lamp, together with a superior arc-lighting system comprising several corollary inventions. Other prominent arc-lighting inventors of the time in the United States included Elihu Thomson and Edwin J. Houston (coworkers), William Wallace, Moses Farmer, Edward Weston, Hiram S. Maxim, Charles Van Depoele, and James J. Wood.

Arc lamps found their most important applications in such fields as street lighting and other outdoor lighting. They were relatively unimportant for general interior illumination.

The final race toward the invention of a practical incandescent lamp seems particularly exciting in retrospect. At the time, the men engaged in the contest were not aware of the detailed progress of their rivals. However, each knew that others were entered in the competition. They all knew that the factors necessary to success were present, if only they could be properly combined.

Dynamos of many kinds had been built, so that a reasonably satisfactory power source was available. It needed improvement, to be sure, but that could come later. The creation of a suitable vacuum had been largely solved by a vacuum pump invented in 1865 by Herman Sprengel, a chemist working in England, though German by birth. (By that time the desirability of creating a vacuum lamp had already become evident.) The only remaining basic need was for an incandescent lamp that would be commercially useful. The production of such a lamp was the obvious goal.

The entrants in the race were seven in number. Two of the men worked as partners, so it was a six-way competition:

Moses G. Farmer, who resumed his work on lamps at this time (1877)

Joseph W. Swan, who also returned to this field of experiment in England

Hiram S. Maxim, a prolific inventor in the fields of machinery, guns, etc.

St. George Lane-Fox, a resourceful English experimenter

William S. Sawyer and Albon Man, who developed a wide variety of lamps

Thomas A. Edison, already known as a leading inventor

All these men created incandescent lamps that surpassed those contrived earlier. But Edison won the race—not as measured by exact time of invention, but by practical and commercial success.

CHAPTER 2

Edison Finds the Answers

THOMAS A. EDISON was a rather late starter in the competition to produce a satisfactory lamp. It was not until the autumn of 1877 that he began work on the problem in his laboratory at Menlo Park, N.J. He was then thirty years old. He had been intensively busy on other inventions.

The delay in attacking the lamp problem, however, merely served to emphasize several qualities that were basic in Edison's character and in his native ability. These attributes made him a formidable contender in any contest among inventors.

While not versed in abstract science, nor much interested in it, he possessed unquestionable genius in the practical application of scientific principles. He was persistent almost to the point of stubbornness. Above all, he believed in his own ability to solve practical problems of invention. Edison sometimes seemed to spur himself to greater efforts by making strong, positive statements to newspapermen about what he intended to accomplish. Then he had to make good his claims—and he did make good.

The Menlo Park laboratory, a two-story frame structure about the size of today's standard U.S. Army barracks building, was well-equipped for its time. Several key assistants worked closely with the inventor. The staff, including skilled and unskilled workmen, totaled nearly a hundred.

Edison's first lamp experiments consisted of passing electric currents through strips of carbonized paper and other forms of carbon. He made these trials mostly to confirm the failures of other inventors. Before long he was rather firmly convinced that carbon

11

was not 'a practical burner for a lamp. He decided to try various metals, particularly platinum.

The lamp activity was interrupted for several months by Edison's development work on the phonograph and by a long vacation period made necessary when his health was temporarily impaired.

In 1878, however, he returned to the lamp problem with renewed enthusiasm. On a visit to the Ansonia, Conn., factory of William Wallace, Edison saw and studied a dynamo developed by Wallace and Moses G. Farmer. These men were associated in an arc-lighting business. Their dynamo greatly interested Edison. He realized that it would be a superior power source for his lamp-development work, and he purchased one of the machines.

DEVISING A COMPLETE SYSTEM

As Edison began more intensive study of the problem, he studied all available information about gas illumination systems. This enabled him to determine the objectives of the electrical system he intended to develop. Then, working with platinum, he created the first lamp on which he obtained a patent (applied for in October, 1878, and granted in April, 1879). This, however, was not a practical lamp for widespread use, being too costly and complicated.

Edison's experiments continued at an accelerated pace. He built somewhat better lamps with platinum burners. He tried several other metals. The intensive effort of the young inventor and all his leading assistants was focused on one elusive secret: What element could be heated to incandescence efficiently and economically? In other words, how could they create an electric lamp that would give abundant light at a cost low enough to compete with gas or kerosene?

Naturally it cost money to carry on this work. To finance further development, Edison turned to a close friend, Grosvenor P. Lowrey, a leading lawyer with an extensive practice among business firms in New York City. Lowrey persuaded several large investors to join in organizing the Edison Electric Light Company. The company was incorporated on Oct. 17, 1878, with capital of

$300,000. This was the beginning of what is now known as the General Electric Company.

As the search for better lamp components continued, Edison pursued further the need for a complete incandescent-lighting *system*. The lamp would be the key element in the system, but many other parts required consideration: dynamos, switches, wiring, meters, etc. How could these best be fitted together into an efficient arrangement of power generation and distribution? The answers to that question would largely determine the design of each component part, including the lamp.

The first answer Edison arrived at was the use of a multiple (or parallel) distribution circuit rather than the series circuit commonly used for arc lighting. This would permit any lamp in the circuit to be operated individually without affecting the operation of the others.

For this, he needed a new type of dynamo—one that would provide constant voltage and thus suit the requirements of the parallel circuit. (Series circuits use constant *current* from the dynamo, rather than constant *voltage*.) So Edison built the dynamo. The principles he employed were entirely new. They were completely opposed to the conceptions of other men working with electricity at the time. His machine reached 90 per cent efficiency in converting mechanical energy to electrical energy. Previously 50 per cent had been regarded as the optimum.

Edison's dynamo produced 110 volts. He had chosen this voltage in preference to the low voltages used by others. Again, his plan proved practical through the years and resulted in great savings in the amount of copper needed for electric cables in the standard distribution systems.

THE FILAMENT IDEA

The next step in Edison's logical development of an incandescent lighting system was highly significant. That was his adoption of a high-resistance filament for the lamp he hoped to develop. A study of the electrical mathematics involved, according to Ohm's law, would show that a high-resistance lamp was essential to successful operation of the system he had visualized. But Ohm's law was still not well understood by electrical experimenters in Edison's time, and practically all the lamps invented earlier had used relatively thick, low-resistance burners.

Consequently, Edison's greatest contribution to lamp design was *the filament idea*—the use of a very thin thread or threadlike wire that would offer high resistance to the passage of electric current. Many disappointments were to follow during the next few months as Edison tried to create a satisfactory lamp, but the filament idea marked the difference that was to lead to eventual success.

Early in 1879 the inventor built his first high-resistance lamps. He obtained patents on two different models, both of which used long thin platinum wire as the filament material. Again the high costs, limited efficiency, and intricate construction of the lamps made them unacceptable commercially. In making them, however, Edison learned much that aided him in further experiments.

THE FIRST SUCCESSFUL LAMP

During the months that followed, Edison returned to carbon as a possible illuminant. In filament form its resistance would be rather high. Its melting point was much higher than that of platinum. (The melting point of platinum was not much higher than the temperature needed to start making it incandescent. Therefore the platinum filament was often destroyed in the effort to get higher incandescence.)

There are, of course, many forms of carbon and it is a constituent of all organic materials. To carbonize a substance, it is heated in a container from which air is excluded. With no oxygen present, the heat does not completely burn the material; a carbon residue remains after other matter has been liberated in the form of various gases.

During the autumn of 1879 the Edison laboratory became practically a carbon factory. Edison and his assistants carbonized literally hundreds of different substances and tested them as high-resistance illuminants. Many of these were fragile and hard to handle, and could not be formed into suitable filaments. But the searchers persisted, trying any and every form of carbon they could devise.

During this incessant activity, Edison determined that the filament he wanted should be no larger than about $\frac{1}{64}$ inch in diameter. This was the size of coarse sewing thread, so he selected several pieces of cotton thread a few inches long and carbonized them by subjecting them to high heat in an airtight crucible placed in a furnace. There were disappointing failures in this process. Other discouragements followed when he tried to clamp the ends of the delicate filament to platinum wires. The wires were to carry current to and from the filament.

Finally this ticklish job was completed. The platinum lead-in wires had previously been sealed in a piece of glass tubing—except, of course, for the ends which were to be joined to the filament by tiny clamps.

Once the inventor and his helpers had mounted the filament in position, looped in hairpin shape, they inserted it in a glass bulb. Then they used flame to fuse the glass tubing (forming the "stem" of the lamp) to the neck of the bulb. This step was called "sealing-in." Next they used a vacuum pump to pull air out of the bulb through a glass tube. This exhaust tube had been fused to the top of the bulb—opposite the neck through which the filament had been inserted.

In working with platinum burners, Edison had made an important discovery. He had found gases and vapors which had been absorbed by the glass bulb and stem and by the metal filament. The heat of lamp operation would free these gases and partially destroy the vacuum unless they could be removed in some way during the lampmaking process. So he had passed a small amount of current through the filament, heating it slightly, during the exhaust process. The released gases could then be pumped out, along with the air inside the bulb. He used the same method now in building the carbon-filament lamp. It took more than eight hours before the pump had created a high vacuum in the bulb. Finally, by the application of heat, the exhaust tube was sealed off from the bulb. Only a small sharp tip on the top of the bulb showed where the exhaust tube and bulb had been connected.

The lamp was now complete: bulb, filament, lead-in wires, and glass stem. The lead-in wires protruded from the sealed glass at the bottom of the bulb, ready to be connected to an electrical circuit. With the exception of a metal base, which was a later development, all the basic features of the incandescent lamps made for years afterward were incorporated in this Edison lamp. Also, for many years the progressive steps in making lamps followed the same pattern as the construction of this lamp in the Menlo Park laboratory. There were a great many refinements and improvements, but the fundamental processes of lamp assembly remained essentially the same.

The time for trial of the new lamp had come. The date was Oct. 19, 1879. Would the slender carbon thread come to incandescence when current was applied? Would it provide enough light to make it a useful and economical source of illumination? Above all, would it last for more than a few minutes—would it operate long enough to be practical for lighting homes, offices, factories, stores, and schools? These were the crucial questions. There had been so many disappointments with earlier efforts that not even those in the laboratory could be optimistic about the probable results.

Edison turned on the current, using an external resistance that would enable him to build up the incandescence little by little. Soon the lamp reached a steady, glowing brightness. As it continued to operate hour after hour, the hopes of the little group of men in the laboratory developed into enthusiastic fulfillment. Almost two full days and nights passed before the lamp burned out. The date usually given as the time of invention of this first commercially practical incandescent lamp was Oct. 21—the day on which the test was completed.

Today a life of 40 hours for a lamp bulb seems ridiculous to us. We are accustomed to rated lives of 750 or 1,000 hours for most incandescent lamps and several thousand hours for fluorescent tubes. But it should be remembered that for many years prior to 1879 the lives of the incandescent lamps invented by a few pioneer experimenters had been measured in minutes rather than hours.

Elated by the success of the tryout, Edison was certain that 40 hours or thereabouts was not the limit of his lamp. He knew he could improve it enough to get 100 hours of life or more.

FIRST APPLICATIONS

The exploration of all available forms of carbon continued. Edison realized that the carbonized cotton thread, with its extreme fragility, would be difficult to manufacture in quantity. As he experimented further, he found that thin carbonized filaments of paper (bristol board) gave superior results. They provided several hundred hours of life and were considerably stronger than the filaments made from thread.

Public announcement of Edison's triumph occupied the entire first page of the New York *Herald* for Sunday, Dec. 21, 1879. The story broke in connection with a public demonstration of the new lamps at Menlo Park on New Year's Eve. Some 60 lamps were mounted on poles in the laboratory grounds and along adjacent streets. Several thousand people witnessed this first showing of the lamps that were to revolutionize the science of lighting.

On Nov. 4, 1879, Edison applied for a patent on his carbon lamp. The patent—No. 223,898—was granted on Jan. 27, 1880. This proved later to be one of the most significant patents ever issued by the U.S. Patent Office.

The first commercial installation of the lamps was made on the new steamship *Columbia*. A total of 115 lamps created a sensation aboard the ship as she sailed on her first voyage from New York City to San Francisco in May, 1880.

In the lithography shop of Hinds, Ketcham & Co., 229 Pearl Street, New York City, the first commercial installation on land totaled 60 lamps. This was early in 1881.

A new industry had been launched. The Edison laboratory and the Edison Electric Light Co. buzzed with activity. Hundreds of details had to be perfected before widespread commerical applications could be arranged.

The prospect of practical incandescent lighting was creating a far greater stir in the financial and business world than the meager installations of 1880 in themselves could justify. The public sensed that the gaslight era had started on its way out. Incandescent electric lighting—the lighting of the future—had captured the imagination of the American people. Nothing could stop it now.

CHAPTER 3

The Mighty Power of a Slender Thread

MANUFACTURING of lamps and the other major parts of the Edison lighting system had to be started from scratch. For a few months the lamps were made in the laboratory, but it soon became obvious that new facilities were needed for manufacture on a larger scale. Late in 1880 Edison formed a separate company, the Edison Lamp Co., and set it up in a small factory building about a half mile from the laboratory. The Edison Electric Light Co. remained the parent company—first for the lamp factory and later for a series of other companies building Edison lighting equipment. Its principal purpose was to promote the system commercially.

An agreement between the Edison Electric Light Co. and the Edison Lamp Co. specified that the lamp factory was to furnish lamps to the parent company at 40 cents each. The factory's capacity was 1,000 lamps per day, but this rate was not achieved for more than a year. This was the first factory of any kind to use electricity for both light and power.

Making the new product at a cost even close to 40 cents, however, remained an unrealized hope for more than three years. Numerous problems had frustrated the laboratory workers as they painstakingly built lamps one by one. Now these difficulties were multiplied in the factory. The shopworkers and the management struggled with a hundred "bugs"—leakage of air into the bulbs, a high rate of breakage, the complications of keeping the brittle filament intact, and so on. It was all handwork and necessarily slow. But the men in the little plant profited by their mistakes and failures. Gradually they learned how to improve each manufacturing process and how to reduce costs. The factory output reached full capacity and still the demand for lamps could not be met. In April, 1882, the company transferred lamp manufacturing to larger quarters in a group of buildings at Harrison, N.J. By late summer of that year the Harrison operation, with 150 employees, was producing 1,200 lamps a day.

For the first year after the public announcement of the lamps, they cost $1.10 each to produce. (This was, essentially, the calendar year 1880.) As efficiency increased during the second year, the cost was 70 cents per lamp. For the third year, 50 cents was the average figure. Finally, in the fourth year of lampmaking, careful management and developing skills brought manufacturing costs down to about 37 cents per lamp. These were bare costs at the factory, including no distribution costs of any kind. Throughout this period the lamps were being sold to the parent company at 40 cents each.

In later years the staff of the Harrison plant, with ever-growing expertness, chipped away at the cost figure bit by bit until it dwindled to 22 cents. (All costs given here refer to the 16-candlepower carbon lamp.) It was a long hard struggle to conquer the annoying problems of precision manufacture. It occurred at a time when there was no high-speed machinery for the purpose and almost no mass-production knowledge anywhere in industry.

This was the first in a long series of similar battles, from 1880 to the present day. All of them had the same objectives: to make lamps better, to make them at lower cost, and to provide more good lighting for the American people. Then as now, of course, certain motives of self-interest also spurred the management and the employees. They wanted to maintain and increase the jobs and the employee incomes in the business. They wanted to earn a reasonable return on the investment of capital in the business, to benefit those who had put up the money. But they recognized that none of these benefits were possible unless the other objectives— the public-service aims of the lamp and lighting business—were kept in first place.

OTHER EDISON COMPANIES

To produce the other components of Edison's lighting system, similar procedures had to be followed. Bergmann & Company in New York City, headed by a former Edison employee, started manufacturing sockets, switches, and other such items early in 1880.

A company organized toward the end of that year took over from the laboratory the task of building Edison's dynamos and other heavy machinery. Known as the Edison Machine Works, it began operations in New York City early in 1881. Five years later the business had outgrown its quarters in Manhattan. In 1886 the management selected Schenectady as a suitable location and transferred the plant to that city. This, then, was the beginning of the Schenectady Works, which has so long been a primary center of General Electric development.

Also in 1881 the Electric Tube Co. began functioning as a part of the expanding Edison enterprises. In a factory on Washington Street, New York City, this company produced underground tubing, junction boxes, and corollary equipment.

Edison firmly believed that the most efficient and economical way to furnish electrical power would be to build central stations. Each of these large generating plants would serve many customers. The alternative was to establish a generator on the premises of each customer. Actually, in the early years both methods were used, but the central-station system soon proved its superiority.

Late in 1880 Edison and his staff drew plans for the first central station, to be located in New York City at 257 Pearl Street. This was a tremendous undertaking at the time. Not only was it necessary to install steam boilers and a hitherto unprecedented array of "Jumbo" dynamos, but also to lay 14 miles of underground cables and install many more miles of wiring in the buildings that were to be lighted. Almost two years passed before the job was finished.

The first central-station company was called the Edison Electric Illuminating Co. of New York. The Pearl Street station

262041

began operations on Sept. 4, 1882. At the start the load of 300 amperes furnished the new lighting to 59 customers, with a total of 1,284 lamp sockets. The full capacity of the six dynamos was about 540 kilowatts. Each of the lamps made at that time consumed approximately 75 watts, so the station could illuminate at most about 7,200 lamps.

After that the building of central stations proceeded rapidly in many American cities. By 1887 there were 60 Edison central-station companies, serving customers with a total of about 150,-000 lamps.

For the direct installations on customers' premises, the Edison Co. for Isolated Lighting was formed in 1882. By the end of that year there were about 150 such installations, with 30,000 lamps in use. Within five years the totals increased to 700 installations and more than 180,000 lamps. Most of these customers, of course, were commercial and industrial firms. The central stations served both these types of business and residential customers as well.

Rounding out the list of Edison lighting companies was the Canadian Edison Mfg. Co., organized in 1882 to sell the system in Canada.

As the market increased, it became possible and beneficial to consolidate the companies. The Edison Machine Works absorbed the Edison Tube Co. in 1883. Three years later the Edison Electric Light Co. took over the Edison Company for Isolated Lighting. Also in 1886 the Edison United Mfg. Co. was formed to handle all phases of the business formerly carried on by the Edison Machine Works, the Edison Lamp Co., and Bergmann & Company.

The complete consolidation of the Edison lighting companies occurred in 1889. The Edison General Electric Co., formed at that time, included all the companies except those operating central stations. It would be far from correct to say that the "growing pains" of the business had ceased, but the hectic period of having to create separate corporations had passed. They had been necessary so that each small group of experts for one major part of the system could concentrate on solving manufacturing problems as independently as possible. Each unit had accomplished this to the point where it was mass-producing satisfactorily and growing at a steady rate. Now they could all take their places in a more cohesive company structure.

LAMP AND LIGHTING IMPROVEMENTS

No matter how sensational the news of the Edison lighting system was in 1880, the success or failure of an entire new industry hung on one slender thread: the carbonized filament the inventor had developed. Other lamp and lighting companies entered the field after 1880, basing their activities on lamps developed by Edison's competitors (Farmer, Sawyer and Man, Lane-Fox, Maxim, and Swan). However, the strengh and efficiency of the Edison filament was to determine whether the public would accept the incandescent lamp as a superior light source.

When regular manufacturing began, Edison and his associates were not content to ride along with a product that was merely good—if it could be made better. Research continued just as intensively as ever after the development of the carbonized-paper filament. The laboratory staff tested almost every conceivable substance. They had tried all the metals then known and available that possessed favorable characteristics for filament use. Now, among other materials, they experimented with fishing line, onion skin, leather, cotton cloth, macaroni, human hair, flour paste, and the fibers of more than 20 varieties of wood.

One day Edison picked up a palm-leaf fan and thoughtfully examined the bamboo binding strip around its edge. He instructed a laboratory assistant to try making filaments from the bamboo fibers, employing the usual carbonizing process. The resultant filaments proved to be much more efficient than carbonized bristol board. They were hard and strong by comparison with the earlier filaments. The lamp factory began making lamps that used carbonized bamboo. As a result, the lamps manufactured in 1880 and 1881 were rated to give 600 hours of life in service. In the latter year the light output of the lamps was also increased as the men in the plant learned how to control the difficult carbonizing process more effectively. Edison sent several men on a world-wide search for the most suitable types of bamboo. Of more than 6,000 different varieties of vegetable fiber tested, only three were found useful for filaments. The bamboo finally chosen came from Japan.

In 1888 the Edison laboratory found that coating the filament with a thin layer of asphalt increased the light output and had the effect of reducing voltage variations. Otherwise, the filaments in Edison lamps until 1894 remained essentially the same as those produced in 1881.

Besides the gradual improvement of filaments, there were several other advances in lampmaking during the first 10 years. This was hand manufacturing. It was difficult and often exasperating work. For instance, the mounting of filaments in the early days posed particularly troublesome problems and resulted in considerable spoilage. Fastening the filaments to the lead-in wires by means of very small clamps resulted in leakage of air, broken filaments, and arcing.

From 1881 to 1886 these failures were materially reduced by copper-plating the filament and lead-in wires together. Further research produced in 1886 a system of using carbon paste for these connections. This was simpler and less costly, and the lamps were more satisfactory in efficiency and voltage control.

At first the Edison Lamp Co. made its glass bulbs from 1-inch tubing. Soon, however, the factory management made arrangements to obtain them from the Corning Glass Works. They were handmade and free-blown by skilled glassmakers who took the glass directly from the furnaces.

The most time-consuming process in the early manufacture of lamps was pumping the air out of the bulb to get a good vacuum. For many months the exhaust time remained at five hours, with the use of Sprengel mercury pumps. An operator handled 50 pumps, with one lamp connected to each pump. Removal of water vapor was the main problem. The moisture adhered to the glass, and so the bulb had to be heated during the exhaust process. Heat liberated the moisture and a chemical preparation gradually absorbed it. A series of improvements in the Sprengel pump radically reduced the exhaust time. By 1885 the five hours had been cut to half an hour—a real achievement credited to the Edison factory engineers.

Lamp bases and sockets presented other problems. The original lamps made in the laboratory used a wooden socket containing two strips of copper. At the lamp base the copper strips were connected to the lead-in wires. The other ends of the strips were tied into the electric circuit by means of wires attached to an ordinary pair of binding posts. It was a cumbersome method. Obviously simpler and better sockets and bases were needed.

Various changes introduced during the next few years evolved finally into the metal screw base and socket that are familiar to all users of incandescent lamps today. By 1888 this method had become standard for Edison lamps, though in later years it was further improved by the use of better cements and insulating materials to create safe, strong bases and sockets.

A lamp-testing department became a necessity as soon as commercial production started. The first test section at the Menlo Park laboratory was superseded in March, 1881, by a well-organized department at the factory, under the supervision of Dr. Edward L. Nichols. In the early years the measurements of lamp performance remained rather crude by modern standards. They consisted mainly of life tests and measurements of operating voltage. For years every lamp had to be measured individually by a photometer to determine its voltage and average candlepower. The diameter and length of each filament varied slightly from the ideal size, and this affected the lamp rating.

The Edison lighting arrangement utilized direct current. One of Edison's most notable contributions was the three-wire system of distribution. This effected a 60 per cent saving in the amount of copper required for distribution of electricity.

Two 110-volt dynamos operated in series to get 220 volts. Two distribution wires were connected to the outside wires from the dynamos. Between these distribution wires the potential was 220 volts. The third, or neutral, wire ran between the other two. It was connected at a point between the two dynamos. Therefore the voltage between the neutral wire and either of the other wires was 110 volts. Lamps were connected between the neutral wire and one of the other wires. Smaller wires could be used with this system than with a two-wire system. The result was a saving of many millions of dollars in central-station investment and in the costs of electricity to consumers during the years before alternating current gained predominance. Edison patented this development in 1883.

COMPETITIVE LIGHTING SYSTEMS

The major lighting market at the time of Edison's first successful lamp was of course in the cities. Gas illumination accounted for about 90 per cent of this market and electric-arc lighting for about 10 per cent. Most of the arc lighting consisted of outdoor applications such as street lighting.

Naturally the change from gas lighting to incandescent electric lighting could not take place overnight, nor in fact for quite a few years. The gas companies remained in competition and fought keenly and skillfully to retain their market.

At the same time, the other inventors and business leaders interested in incandescent lighting were far from idle during the first 10 years of the Edison system's development. Edison's success stimulated all of them to greater activity. Sawyer and Man, Farmer, Maxim, and the others had tried to "get there first" with a commercially practical lamp. Now they felt that Edison's victory simply proved that the race had been worth running—and so why not enter the next event on the program? They continued their development work and obtained patents on lamps that differed somewhat from Edison's basic lamp.

It is not necessary here to trace in detail the growth of the other incandescent lighting companies. A summary at the end of the chapter indicates the major competitors of the time and the extensive program of consolidation occurring between 1880 and 1890.

Throughout this period the complications of corporate structure in the industry were matched by the intricacies of the patent situation. No one of the inventors could be certain that his lamp patents would be sustained in a legal conflict between companies, though Edison's priority seemed clear. Besides lamps, there was also a multiplicity of patents for other equipment used in lighting systems. In the first few years (1880–1885) the effort was not to see whether "the other fellow" might be infringing in some way. Instead, all were intent on getting into commercial production and building business.

Two major groups of companies emerged from the consolidations and became the leading competitors of the Edison system. One was led by George Westinghouse, a prolific inventor and successful manufacturer of railroad and electrical equipment. His main company was known (after 1889) as the Westinghouse Electric & Mfg. Co.

The Thomson-Houston Electric Co. and its affiliated companies comprised the other group. Originally formed to manufacture and sell the arc-lighting equipment developed by Elihu Thomson and Edwin J. Houston, the company soon became prominent in incandescent lighting as well. Its leader and president was Charles A. Coffin, an exceptionally able and farsighted businessman, while Thomson directed the company's engineering work.

In 1888 the Thomson-Houston and Westinghouse companies entered into a general cross-licensing agreement. Thomson-Houston licensed Westinghouse to make and sell equipment covered by Thomson-Houston patents—and vice versa. Various companies in the two groups held title to inventions made by Maxim, Farmer, and Edward Weston. However, the lamp patents most useful to both groups at this time were those of Sawyer and Man.

Meantime, the business of the Edison companies continued to grow. Lamp production was being stepped up year by year. The manufacture of other equipment kept pace. Thousands of new installations and the building of new Edison central stations kept an ever-increasing number of workers busy with the task of relighting the United States. The little thread of carbonized material was in fact sustaining a new industry just as Edison and his coworkers had foreseen during their 40-hour vigil in the laboratory in 1879.

Major Electric Lighting Companies (Other than Edison Companies)
1880–1890

United States Electric Lighting Co., organized in 1878. This company held patents issued to Hiram Maxim, Moses Farmer, and Edward Weston.

Consolidated Electric Light Co., organized in 1882 as the successor to two earlier companies. Consolidated later held patents issued to Sawyer and Man, through the Sawyer-Man Electric Co., an affiliate organized in 1887. (The Consolidated company mentioned here should not be confused with an enterprise organized many years later and known as the Consolidated Electric Lamp Co.)

Brush Electric Co., founded in 1880 by Charles F. Brush, long a leader in arc-lighting development. Brush purchased rights to the Lane-Fox lamp patents, and later changed to lamps that had been developed by Joseph W. Swan.

Union Switch & Signal Co., organized in 1882 by George Westinghouse. The company name was changed to the Westinghouse Electric Co. in 1886 and in 1889 to the Westinghouse Electric & Mfg. Co.

Thomson-Houston Electric Co., organized in 1883. This company was an important factor in the arc-lighting business, holding the patents of Elihu Thomson and Edwin J. Houston. It also made incandescent lamps based on Sawyer and Man patents.

Swan Lamp Mfg. Co., organized in 1885 to manufacture and sell incandescent lamps invented by Joseph W. Swan.

Consolidations

In 1888 the Westinghouse company purchased United States Electric Lighting Co., Consolidated, Sawyer-Man, and the Waterhouse Electric & Mfg. Co.

The Thomson-Houston company controlled Consolidated and Sawyer-Man from 1884 until the sale of those companies to Westinghouse. Thomson-Houston purchased four companies that were best known for arc lighting: the Van Depoele Electric Mfg. Co. and the Fort Wayne Electric Light Co., both in 1888, and the Brush Electric Co. and the Schuyler Electric Co. in 1889.

PART TWO

Building a New Industry

CHAPTER 4

The Formation of the
General Electric Company

THE EARLY GROWTH of most modern industries involves patents. This is natural, since the inventor or developer of a new product normally tries to protect his interests by obtaining patents, and the purpose of the patent system is to encourage invention. The lighting industry was no exception to the usual pattern. The nature of the industry led inherently to hundreds of patentable devices. From 1885 on, patent conflicts multiplied; they had to be settled if the industry was to maintain orderly growth.

Since the incandescent lamp was the heart of the new lighting, it was important to all manufacturers to arrive at some determination in regard to basic lamp patents. Incandescent-lamp production for 1885 totaled about 300,000 lamps, but no one needed a crystal ball to see that annual output would soon be measured in millions. The Edison Electric Light Co. was by far the leading supplier. However, new companies were springing up every year. Some of them made lamps that did not appear to copy the Edison product, while others were infringing, knowingly or otherwise. The directors of the company decided that it was time to take action. They must take steps to establish the validity of the lamp patent granted to Edison in January, 1880.

A patent is, in effect, a legal monopoly on a product or process, granted by the government for a limited period of years. In the United States, the term is 17 years. The inventor, by applying for a patent, makes public the information involved in his invention.

31

In exchange for this he receives the right to exclude all others from making, using, and selling the invention during the life of the patent. These rights he can transfer to others, either by direct sale or by means of a licensing agreement.

Like other patents, Edison's lamp patent represented a fundamental property right. When the company started legal action to establish the validity of its patents, it was moving in the same direction as several other companies in the industry. Most of the leaders in the field discovered about 1885 that patent problems existed for almost all major parts of a complete lighting system. Undoubtedly, however, the legal establishment of the ownership of the basic lamp patent was the most important matter to be decided.

Therefore the Edison Electric Light Co. brought suit against the United States Electric Lighting Co. in 1885. This turned out to be the key action in a series of legal contests aimed at discouraging patent infringement. The suit posed two basic questions : Was the Edison lamp patent valid, as described in the application and patent ? Was the patent being infringed (in this case, by the United States company) ?

There was a long delay in bringing the case to trial. At last the hearing began—in October, 1889—in the U.S. Circuit Court for the Southern District of New York. Judge William Wallace presided. More months passed in arguing the case and presenting testimony. Then in July, 1891, Judge Wallace determined that the Edison patent was valid and infringed. The United States company appealed, and in October, 1892, the U.S. Circuit Court of Appeals sustained the judgment handed down by Judge Wallace.

Perhaps the most meaningful finding in the trial proceedings concerned the priority of Edison's work with a *filament* type of burner. The high-resistance carbon thread marked his lamp as essentially different from lamps employing pencil-sized carbon rods. The Maxim lamps manufactured by the United States company used threadlike filaments, and so were held to be infringements. This underlined once more the importance of Edison's filament idea.

During the seven years consumed by the legal action, the number of competitors in the lamp business had steadily increased. In 1890 more than 30 manufacturers were making incandescent lamps. The Edison company's share of total lamp sales fell far below the 1885 figure.

Since most of the competitive manufacturers were infringing the basic patent, the Edison company brought a number of suits and obtained injunctions forbidding continuance of the practice. It was impossible to prevent all such infringements. All through the nineties, companies entered and left the lamp business at a rapid rate. However, the most serious violations of the Edison patent, in terms of volume of production, were ended. Other leading producers, such as Westinghouse, developed noninfringing lamps, and competition remained active. The net effect of the patent suits was not to reduce the number of lamp manufacturers (which remained well above 30 for several years after 1892) but to stimulate the creation of new types of lamps.

EDISON—THOMSON-HOUSTON MERGER

During 1891 and early 1892 the managements of the Edison General Electric Co. and the Thomson-Houston Electric Co. carried on negotiations with a view toward consolidating the companies. This was much the most significant corporate development in the electrical industry up to that time. The two groups finally arrived at an agreement and on April 15, 1892, they met together to create the General Electric Company.

Both companies were strong leaders in the industry. Each possessed highly developed physical facilities—factories, laboratories, engineering departments. Most important of all, they could bring together an unparalleled array of individual talents: men adept at sales and financial management, others who led in engineering and product development, and many more who were skilled in the mechanical arts so essential to successful mass production. Furthermore, to a large extent the two groups complemented rather than duplicated each other. In most departments Thomson-Houston had the over-all edge in factory management and operating methods; the Edison company was particularly strong in commercial development through district sales offices.

The Edison company brought into the combination such major assets as the fundamental incandescent-lamp patents and the Edison system of distributing electrical energy. Thomson-Houston contributed its profitable arc-lighting business plus valuable developments in alternating-current systems, principally those devised by Elihu Thomson. The Edison company had missed opportunities to progress in alternating-current work, largely because of the reluctance of the inventor himself to accept these systems in preference to direct current.[1]

In total annual sales, the Edison and Thomson-Houston companies stood closely comparable, each accounting for more than $10 million in gross business for the year 1891. With the growth of the electric traction business as well as lighting, the Edison company employed some 6,000 people and Thomson-Houston about 4,000.

GENERAL ELECTRIC LEADERS, 1892

The new General Electric Company began active operation on June 1, 1892. Lamp manufacturing was soon concentrated at Harrison, N.J., rather than in the Thomson-Houston plant at Lynn, Mass. Edison himself had by this time left the lamp business very largely in the hands of others. He preferred to explore new problems of invention in other fields.

The manager of the Harrison Works was Francis R. Upton, one of Edison's top assistants in the early experimental work. Known for his great ability in applying the mathematics of electricity, Upton had assumed management of the lamp factory in 1880, its first year of operation.

John W. Howell held the position of chief engineer at the Harrison Works. At this time Howell was in the early years of a most distinguished career in lamp manufacturing. It was he who worked

---

[1] Alternating-current systems, which enormously extended the range of the central station, had been successfully demonstrated by William Stanley in 1886 at Great Barrington, Mass., but Westinghouse was the first company to exploit Stanley's ideas commercially.

out the first steps in mass production of lamps—for instance, the improvements that reduced the time for exhausting air from the bulbs from five hours to 30 minutes. And it was Howell who developed the first machines that started to transform lampmaking from a hand industry to a mechanical industry.

Incidentally, John Howell was a significant figure during the trial of the Edison company's infringement suit on the basic lamp patent. The counsel for the United States company contended that the description of Edison's patent was insufficient—that it would not enable anyone "skilled in the art" to make incandescent lamps. Howell made 27 lamps by hand, following the information given in the patent. On the witness stand he told how he had made them and offered to repeat the performance in court. The judge, apparently convinced, decided that Howell had proved the point without having to set up a small lamp factory in the courtroom.

The Edison company had established district sales offices in 1890 and begun to build an effective field organization. Perhaps the best-known lamp and lighting sales representatives in this group were Arthur H. Bush, specializing in central-station sales, and Sidney B. Paine, who worked principally with the so-called isolated plants.

The Thomson-Houston company in 1891 had made 870 central-station installations. The Edison company served 375 central stations, most of them larger than those of Thomson-Houston. In isolated plants, the Edison total was about 2,300; Thomson-Houston had not worked much at this type of business and served less than 50 installations.

At Schenectady the Edison Machine Works now comprised more than 25 buildings. John Kruesi, the works manager, had been, like Upton, a close associate of Edison from the start of the inventor's lighting activities.

Several top-management men in the new General Electric Company came from Thomson-Houston. Elihu Thomson and Edwin J. Houston had experimented with arc lighting while teaching general science at the Boys' Central High School in Philadelphia. During the years 1879–1881 they started manufacturing the components of the arc-lighting system they had developed. This was in

New Britain, Conn., and the company was known as the American Electric Co. Thomson remained active in this business after 1881, while Houston kept his teaching position. American Electric failed to gain much of the arc-lighting market. The little company needed better sales representation. Then in 1882 a man named Charles A. Coffin became interested and entered the company, which was reorganized as the Thomson-Houston Electric Co.

Coffin was a shoe manufacturer in Massachusetts—a dynamic leader especially skilled in commercial development. As the head of a group of financial backers, he set up the Thomson-Houston company in a new plant in Lynn, Mass., in 1883. The principal products at first were dynamos and arc lamps, with expansion into incandescent lighting coming along a little later. Thomson and Coffin worked together in great harmony, with Thomson supervising engineering while Coffin handled top-management duties.

Another important member of the top group in Thomson-Houston had been a leading pupil of Elihu Thomson in his Philadelphia classes. His name was Edwin W. Rice, Jr., and as soon as he joined the company he demonstrated his rare ability in scientific research and development.

Rice, as general superintendent from 1885 to 1892, was also fortunate to have the services of two capable executive assistants to help him build Thomson-Houston's manufacturing capacity. One was George Emmons, the factory manager, who was later to manage the Schenectady Works for many years. The other, Albert H. Rohrer, held the position of assistant engineer. In later years, as manufacturing superintendent for General Electric from 1892 to 1923, Rohrer won particular recognition for the "Test" course he established to develop personnel for all G-E departments. This unique activity, begun with Coffin's enthusiastic backing, was perhaps the first systematic program for training promising young employees in a variety of phases of a business before assigning them to specific jobs.

There were other men prominent in the progress of the two companies at the time G.E. was organized—men who represented assets at least as important as the property values involved. Furthermore, there were able foremen, skilled mechanics, valuable employees in the ranks. In a specialized history emphasizing the lamp business, they obviously cannot all be mentioned.

Coffin was elected president of the new company. With Eugene Griffin, a Thomson-Houston man, as executive vice-president, Rice was also named as a vice-president and carried the additional title of technical director. Thomson headed the engineering laboratory at Lynn.

Leading business and banking personalities of Boston and New York City made up the first board of directors. Besides Coffin, Griffin, and Edison, the directors were: F. L. Ames, T. Jefferson Coolidge, Jr., C. H. Coster, F. S. Hastings, Henry L. Higginson, D. O. Mills, J. Pierpont Morgan, and Hamilton McK. Twombly (chairman).

PROGRESS DESPITE BUSINESS DEPRESSION

Meshing two sizable companies into one smoothly running organization always presents problems. Operation during the first few months resembles the "shakedown cruise" of a Navy battleship. How capable will the leadership be at every level? Will the entire crew work easily together with the pride and satisfaction that comes with creating something new? Usually the answers develop fairly early. Consequently a look at the first annual report of the General Electric Company holds considerable interest today in assessing the early results.

Dated Jan. 31, 1893, the report covered seven months' operation—from June 1, 1892, to Jan. 1, 1893. Central stations using Edison and Thomson-Houston apparatus numbered 1,277, supplying electricity to about 2½ million incandescent lamps and 110,-000 arc lamps. The company received royalties from the central-station companies amounting to nearly $2 million per year.

G.E. served 435 electric-railway companies, with 8,836 trolley cars in operation over 4,927 miles of track. The use of electricity for traction was spreading rapidly. Among the annual report's announcements, made as breathlessly as such a document permitted, was this: The company was building electric locomotives—1,600-horsepower giants, no less—and was also manufacturing equip-

ment for an elevated electric railway 6 miles long for the Chicago
World's Fair, the Columbian Exposition of 1893.

As these and other industrial uses increased—factory motors,
for example—they placed load on the lines during the daytime,
with lighting as the chief nighttime load. Formerly the central-
station generators had started spinning at sundown. They eased
up after midnight and closed down when the sun rose. Now the
daytime uses kept many of them working around the clock. Unit
costs of electricity decreased as a result, and so did the price per
kilowatt-hour to the consumer.

During these early months the manufacturing operations of the
Edison company and the Thomson-Houston company had continued as separate enterprises for the most part. The General
Electric Company purchased and distributed their products. Sales
and some other departments had been consolidated in G.E.

Total net profits of the combined operations for the seven-
month period covered by the first annual report amounted to
nearly $3 million. The directors retained one-third of this, over
and above dividends to stockholders, for further development
work and capital investment. It was fortunate for the immediate
future of the company that they did so. It was also fortunate that
General Electric was well supplied with alert leadership, especially
in the person of Charles Coffin, for in 1893 American business entered a period of deep depression.

The economic crisis continued for about five years. Many companies failed, and the entire electrical industry was hard hit. This
was a severe test of Coffin's generalship. Many of the members of
his board did not agree with the financial policies he adopted to
weather the storm and were skeptical that the company could survive. However, they finally voted approval for his plans to dispose
of large blocks of central-station company securities. These had
been accepted in earlier years in part payment for the equipment
needed to establish the central stations. Coffin disposed of them
at a loss, but the money received enabled General Electric to remain solvent.

The company entered into a cross-licensing agreement with
Westinghouse in 1896. This did not include lamp patents but cov-

ered other types of electrical equipment, such as generators and transformers. As in the earlier patent confusion, many companies in the industry found it extremely difficult to install complete electrical systems without the possibility of infringing on another company's patents in regard to some of the equipment. The General Electric–Westinghouse agreement enabled both companies to make such installations freely, each paying the other royalties for the use of certain equipment where necessary. The agreement recognized that General Electric had contributed 62½ per cent of the value of the patents involved, and Westinghouse 37½ per cent.

The production of incandescent lamps climbed steadily despite the economic depression. As output rose, unit costs declined and the prices of the lamps were lowered. From 1880 to 1887 the selling price of the 16-candlepower carbon lamp stood at $1.00. Almost all of these lamps were sold by the manufacturers to the central-station companies rather than to the general public.

Total output of incandescent lamps in the United States during 1891 was about 7½ million. Throughout the nineties the year-by-year figures moved upward, so that by 1899 the manufacturers turned out 25 million lamps. As in other difficult depression times that followed periodically, electric lighting prospered even though business generally suffered. The reasons were: (1) public acceptance and demand for better illumination, and (2) wise management, which passed along to consumers their share of the benefits of mass production, technical progress, and capable business leadership.

CHAPTER 5

From Hands to Machines for
Making Lamps

BESIDES THE DEVELOPMENTS in company organization, the
period after 1890 was characterized by technological improvements that materially advanced the science of lighting. This was true not only in incandescent lighting, but to some
extent in gas and electric-arc illumination as well.

The Welsbach mantle, invented by the Austrian, Carl von Welsbach, caused a resurgence of gas illumination for several years
after 1893. While the invention had been made 10 years earlier,
the mantle was not perfected for some time and did not come into
widespread usage until the late nineties. It provided much better
light than previous gas installations and reduced the cost of gas
lighting drastically—more than 60 per cent.

Other improvements in this type of illumination followed, so
that gas lighting remained a part of the industry picture for about
17 more years. Nevertheless, it declined in importance with every
step forward in the technology of electric lighting.

As for arc lighting, three milestones marked its progress: the
enclosed arc, the so-called flaming arc, and the luminous (or magnetite) arc lamp.

The first commercially practical enclosed-arc lamps (using glass
globes around the carbons) came into use in 1893. William Jandus
of Cleveland, Ohio, invented one type and Louis B. Marks of New
York City developed another. These lamps greatly lengthened the

life of the carbons and offered several other advantages. More interior installations became feasible. General Electric purchased
the rights to the Marks patents and promoted the use of enclosed-
arc lamps for several years.

About 1900 a German experimenter, Hugo Bremer, developed
the flaming arc. He applied various metallic salts to the carbons.
The result was a brilliant arc with a remarkably high light output—
more than 30 lumens per watt for yellow light and more than 15
lpw for white light.[1] Due to short life of the carbons, however,
the flaming-arc lamp received little sales promotion in the United
States. Where used, it found most frequent application in street
lighting.

The magnetite arc was one of the many General Electric developments for which Charles P. Steinmetz was chiefly responsible.
Steinmetz had emigrated to the United States from Germany in
1889. A genius in mathematics and electrical design, he had started
work in this country as a $12-a-week draftsman. Some time later
Elihu Thomson and Edwin W. Rice heard him speak at a meeting
of the American Institute of Electrical Engineers. He made such a
striking impression on them that they persuaded him to come to
work for G.E.

Because it combined high efficiency with long life, economical
operation, and relatively easy maintenance, the magnetite arc won
a favorable position. Magnetite, an iron oxide, composed the
lower electrode of the lamp and produced the high light output—
about 15 lumens per watt in a long-life lamp and up to 25 lpw in a
type designed for shorter life.

General Electric maintained its place at the top of the arc-lighting field as long as the carbon-arc lamp held any appreciable share
of the lighting market—that is, until about 1910. The other companies most influential in arc lighting included the Jandus Electric
Co., Westinghouse, and Western Electric.

[1] The efficiency of a light source means its light output per unit of power consumed. It is measured in *lumens per watt*. Edison's lamp utilizing a carbonized
bamboo filament (1881) had an efficiency of 1.68 lumens per watt, and the best
carbon-filament lamps ever made had efficiencies of 3 to 4 lpw.

MORE EFFICIENCY AND UNIFORMITY

Today's G-E lamp employees would be startled and amused to see how incandescent lamps were made during the first 25 years of manufacture. No intricate high-speed machines aided John Howell and his associates in the Harrison Works at that time. The problem was to devise simple machines, each of which would "act like a pair of hands" to perform one or two small parts of the manufacturing process.

Yet the main objectives were the same then as they are now and always have been in G-E lamp plants and laboratories: more *efficient* lamps, more *uniform* lamps.

Efficiency (light output per unit of electric power) bears a very definite relationship to the expected life of an incandescent lamp. It is an inverse relationship. In the ordinary household bulb, the more light the lamp gives per watt, the shorter its rated life. Conversely, if the lamp is built for longer life, its light output at any given time must be lower. It is not difficult to make a lamp that will burn several times as long as those you buy for your home, most of which are rated at 750 or 1,000 hours of life. Such a lamp, however, would be much dimmer than the ones you use. It would be very unsatisfactory in quantity of illumination. The same type of lamp could be made to burn brighter than a standard bulb, but only at a sacrifice in life. It would have to be replaced by a new lamp much sooner. The household bulbs on the market have been carefully designed to combine high efficiency with a satisfactory life.

For various special purposes, the consumer may want a brilliant light for a short time—for example, a photoflood lamp, used in photography, with a rated life of a few hours. Another customer may want special types in which long life is much more important than light output. At this extreme, for instance, there is the infrared heat lamp, with a rated life of over 5,000 hours and a very low output of visible light. There are dozens of examples in the range between photofloods and heat lamps. In each case, the real need is for a proper balance between light output and lamp life, in accordance with the major uses of each type of lamp.

Once a satisfactory life has been determined for the lamps most commonly used, the lamp manufacturer keeps trying anything and everything likely to increase efficiency within that rated life. So it was that the men in the Harrison Works made improvements whenever they could to get higher light output from their carbon lamps. The rated life they settled on as the best for a carbon lamp was 600 hours, though in actual use most of the lamps burned much longer. Over the years from 1881 to 1906, they were able to increase initial lamp efficiency from 1.68 to 3.4 lumens per watt: about twice as much light for the current consumed during the same lamp life.

Uniformity of the lamps produced in a factory has always rated just as much attention as lamp efficiency. The ideal is to make every lamp equal to all the others produced—equal in strength, in precise dimensions of every part, in the lamp's light output, and in its life. Short of the somewhat impossible ideal, the goal is to make lamps so that a very small percentage of them will fail in any way before they should. (In any random sample lot of 1,000 G-E lamps, some will continue to perform longer than the set standard. This more than counterbalances the few that may fail to meet the ratings.)

PROGRESS BY THE PIONEERS

Sawyer and Man provided one of the earliest improvements in filaments. They discovered a process for treating lamp filaments which was called "flashing" and which they patented in 1879. In essence this process consisted of placing the filament in a glass bottle filled with gasoline vapor and then heating the filament by passing current through it. The filament was connected to an electric circuit by means of clamps fixed in the bottle stopper. The heat decomposed the gasoline vapor; a coating of graphite, separated out of the vapor, was deposited on the filament. (This description omits the detailed steps required in the operator's work.) The flashing of filaments created a superior product, with considerably higher efficiency and better control over filament resistance and lamp voltage.

Other manufacturers used this process from 1880 on. After 1892 the Harrison factory also started filament treatment. Since Thomson-Houston had held rights to the Sawyer and Man patent, General Electric was entitled to use it. John Howell devised an automatic treating machine that speeded the operation and controlled it better than the operator could by hand. The machine enabled the Edison Lamp Works to make lamps that tested better than those produced at the Thomson-Houston plant at Lynn. This was the deciding factor that led General Electric to concentrate lamp production at Harrison.

The only carbon filaments made at first were those created by carbonizing some substance already existing in a fibrous form, and so retaining that form (cotton thread, paper strips, bamboo fibers, etc.). Then various English and American research men began to ask themselves: Why not reduce a suitable substance to a homogeneous mass by soaking it in a solution, then squirt it through a fine die, dry it, and use the resulting "thread" for filaments?

Swan worked on this. So did Edward Weston, for lamps made by the Westinghouse company. Perhaps the best method was developed in 1888 by Leigh S. Powell, an English experimenter.

Powell dissolved cotton in hot zinc chloride. Then, as the soft mass of material was squirted through a die, it fell into alcohol, which hardened it. Washed several times in water to remove the zinc chloride, the thread was then wound on drums and dried. The result was an evenly wound, strong filament material that could be cut to any desired length before carbonizing.

Squirted cellulose filaments made in this way—"the best carbon filaments ever made"—were used in practically all carbon lamps made in the United States in 1894, the year in which General Electric first adopted them.

Skilled handwork continued to govern the making of glass bulbs. Even though output soared to thousands of lamps per day, no one could figure out how to make bulbs by machine. So the glassblowers continued to wield their blowpipes, though they blew the glass into molds instead of employing the old free-blowing system. (The Edison Lamp Works was slow in changing to this method, and began using molded bulbs only after 1892.)

However, once the bulbs were made, a superior method of exhausting the air could be employed by the late nineties. This was a great improvement in terms of time-saving, uniformity, and better lamp performance.

It began in Udine, Italy, where an engineer named Arturo Malignani built an electric lighting plant for the town and made his own lamps. He could not get a good vacuum with the mechanical pumps available to him, but suddenly he discovered a way to improve the vacuum by chemical means.

He coated the inside of the exhaust tube with red phosphorus. Then he heated the filament electrically to high incandescence, and also heated the exhaust tube. The phosphorus vaporized and the vapor entered the bulb. There, for a short time, it created a vivid blue glow. A much better vacuum resulted. The reasons for this were not apparent and are not perfectly understood even today. However, it appears that the phosphorus "cleaned up" vapors and gases remaining in the lamp, so that they were absorbed on the glass wall of the bulb. The action was physical rather than chemical, though it was accomplished by introducing the chemical agent phosphorus, as noted above.

Malignani made his discovery in 1894. It seems to have been one of those happy accidents that abound in the record of scientific progress. In any case, no one argued much about how the vacuum was improved—the important fact was that it did improve.

When G-E officials heard of Malignani's exhaust process, they made a reservation on the first and fastest ship to Italy. Then they told John Howell that he had won the privilege of making the trip. His mission was to buy the American rights to the Malignani process.

Howell regarded the prospect of a free trip to Europe with little or no enthusiasm. When asked why, he is reputed to have said: "I don't think I'll have as much pleasure in marrying this company as I would have had by marrying my girl."

True enough, Howell was slated to be married—on a date chosen by the bride, in accordance with custom. It was a day on which, by the company's reckoning, he would be otherwise occupied: getting Arturo Malignani's signature on an important piece of paper. The town of Udine was beautifully situated. Its Gothic town hall and fifteenth-century castle afforded a fine view of the Austrian Alps—but both stood a considerable distance from any church in the state of New Jersey. However, Howell rearranged his personal affairs to suit the needs of his work. He persuaded his bride to move up the wedding date.

Howell sailed as scheduled and obtained the American rights to Malignani's process. Further refinements by Edison Lamp Works engineers greatly improved the method during the next seven years. Exhaust time dropped to one minute, and 10 lamps at a time could be exhausted on the same equipment, instead of one at a time.

The first modern glassworking machine employed in lampmaking appeared in 1895–1896. It was a sealing-in machine, designed to seal the stem (holding the lead-in wires and the filament) to the neck of the bulb. Thus the stem was placed permanently in position inside the bulb, this being the last step in manufacture before the exhaust process. Two men working for the Buckeye Electric Co. in Cleveland, Ohio, devised such a machine. Then Howell greatly improved it and started using it at Harrison in 1896. This four-head vertical sealing-in machine rotated the work, heating the glass in three positions to prepare it for sealing. An unskilled operator could now complete the sealing-in process for 600 lamps a day, more than twice the previous output. Because the machine handled each lamp in exactly the same way—something that could not be accomplished by hand—greater uniformity of product also resulted.

During the next few years developments in lampmaking machinery followed in rapid succession. Engineers of the Edison Lamp Works won credit for much of this ingenious work. Howell now had a gifted partner in machine invention and the perfection of manufacturing processes: William R. Burrows. Burrows had started in the business as an apprentice at the Thomson-Houston plant in Lynn. After the consolidation of the Edison and Thomson-Houston companies, he worked at Harrison and advanced steadily as he demonstrated his ability in the shop.

The team of Howell and Burrows contrived a stem-making

machine in 1901. Like the sealing-in machine, this was a four-head vertical mechanism. It enabled an unskilled operator to make more than twice as many stems a day as a skilled handworker could produce.

In 1903 Burrows built a tubulating machine, the purpose of which was to blow a hole in the glass (softened by heat) in the rounded end of the bulb—and then to weld the exhaust tube to the bulb at the same point. This prepared the lamp for the exhaust process.

Improvements in bases came along at the turn of the century also. Instead of the plaster of paris formerly used as the insulating material binding the brass base to the neck of the bulb, porcelain came into use in 1900. A waterproof cement was employed with the porcelain. Then, a year later, Alfred Swan of General Electric worked out a method for insulating with glass rather than porcelain. These changes produced a much stronger bulb, and one more suitable to outdoor use as well as inside applications.

Prior to 1900 the various manufacturers utilized more than 175 types of bases and sockets. With nearly 50 million sockets in the United States, the diversity of styles presented continuous problems. Most of these sockets (about 70 per cent) were of the Edison screw type. The others included a wide variety of bayonet types and other designs, each suitable only for the lamps made by one manufacturer. In the face of this situation, troublesome to consumers and to the industry as well, the lamp manufacturers cooperated in a standardization program. The Edison screw base and socket offered the easiest on which to agree. Within less than five years, by concerted action, the companies in the industry brought about a complete standardization of bases and sockets.

Throughout this period the trend was toward systems using alternating current rather than direct current. Larger areas could be served by central stations supplying alternating current. Transformers could step up the voltage for transmission over long distances; then other transformers could step down the voltage in local distribution areas to the relatively low pressure needed for incandescent lighting systems.

William Stanley, the pioneer in alternating-current systems and the leading figure in their development from 1891 to 1899, had worked with Westinghouse in the early years. George Westinghouse had recognized the advantages of alternating-current systems, and Stanley contributed much to Westinghouse lighting expansion by his work on transformers and other equipment.

Stanley left Westinghouse in 1899 with a close associate, Cummings C. Chesney, to form the Stanley Electric Mfg. Co. in Pittsfield, Mass. This was in 1890. Later John F. Kelly joined the team of Stanley and Chesney. These three led the Stanley company in aggressive and successful alternating-current development.

General Electric utilized alternating-current equipment for practically all its central-station installations from 1894 on. Thomson's work with transformers, coupled with early development by the Brush company, enabled G.E. to swing toward alternating current. The move became complete in 1903 when General Electric purchased the Stanley company.

By 1905 the carbon lamp had been brought to its highest pitch of efficiency. The lamp manufacturers, especially the Edison Lamp Works, had made major advances in production methods since 1895. To be sure, they had not gone entirely from hands to machines in making lamps. There was still plenty of hand operation in one stage or another of lampmaking. But several of the most intricate steps had been placed on an automatic or semi-automatic basis. One of the results of this was the employment of more and more women in the lamp factories.

The machine age in the industry, then, had well begun. This was no accident, having come about largely through the skill and training of General Electric's engineers, mechanics, and other factory workers. But it was indeed fortunate that the company's manufacturing facilities and its management were ready to handle future challenges. For new technical and research developments were at hand in the lamp business—greater by far than anything the industry's pioneers had yet seen.

CHAPTER 6

A New Contender in the Lighting Field

ENTERING the incandescent lamp business was not difficult during the first 20 years after Edison's 1879 invention. It required only a modest amount of capital and a small factory. So it was not surprising that many alert businessmen, eager to take advantage of the tremendous public demand, established themselves in this promising new field.

However, reaping profits from lampmaking presented many more complications for most manufacturers than they had found in starting their businesses. The lively competition had brought down the prices of lamps. There was a definite need for better production and engineering. In an effort to improve operations in the industry, General Electric and six other companies organized the Incandescent Lamp Manufacturers Association in 1896. The other companies in the group were the Sunbeam Incandescent Lamp Co., Chicago; the Columbia Incandescent Lamp Co., St. Louis; the Buckeye Electric Co., Cleveland; the Bryan-Marsh Co., Marlboro, Mass.; the Perkins Electric Switch Co., Hartford, Conn.; and the Adams-Bagnall Electric Co., Cleveland. During the next few years 10 other companies joined the association.

One natural consequence of meeting together from time to time was that the heads of these companies grew to know each other better than ever before. They had fought tooth and nail for business, often without any personal contact between themselves. Now they learned that their interests were similar.

In particular, two of the men gradually generated a friendship

49

that was to produce an entirely new and extremely important development in the lamp business. Their names were Franklin S. Terry and Burton G. Tremaine.

TERRY AND TREMAINE

Both these men were in their late thirties in 1901, and both were experienced businessmen. Terry had been in the lamp business in and around Chicago since 1890 as president of the Sunbeam Incandescent Lamp Co. Tremaine conducted an insurance and real-estate business in Cleveland, beginning in 1884, and became interested in lamp manufacturing in 1889. At that time he helped to organize the Fostoria Incandescent Lamp Co. at Fostoria, Ohio. His cousin, H. A. Tremaine, was associated with him in this venture. Other officers of the company were J. B. Crouse and J. Robert Crouse, father and son. The group also owned a glass factory—the Fostoria Bulb and Bottle Co. The Crouses and H. A. Tremaine had previously managed a carbon business, making carbons for arc lamps, which they had sold out to the National Carbon Co. before forming the Fostoria companies.

Terry, an imaginative, enthusiastic business idealist, spent much of his time in 1900 and early 1901 considering the situation of his own lamp company and the others like it. There were more than 30 small manufacturers in the country. They all needed better research, better engineering, and more working capital. Without more strength in all these departments they could not make lamps that equaled the products of the leaders on such vital points as efficiency and uniformity.

Fired by the conception of a group of companies cooperating for the benefit of all, Terry went to call on the men at Fostoria. In a long discussion with B. G. Tremaine, he won support. Together the two men worked out the plan.

By bringing together a number of the smaller companies, they reasoned, they could establish an engineering department that would serve all the lamp factories in the group. This department would have much better staff and equipment than any single small company could maintain as an engineering section. It could conduct basic lamp research and development; it could work out improved manufacturing methods and build better machines; it could offer a "trouble-shooting" service for any affiliated lamp factory that might be struggling with production problems. All the factories would contribute to the maintenance of the engineering department. In turn, all of them would benefit by its facilities—*not on a mandatory basis, but on request from the factory managers,* if and when they desired such assistance.

This cardinal principle came primarily from Terry's thinking. He wanted to build a central organization, but he was firmly opposed to centralized control. This sounded paradoxical but it was not. Terry's idea was that a headquarters group should *serve* the factory managers, the sales staffs in the field, and the other workers in all departments who best understood the local problems they faced. So the plan included sales and advertising counsel, credit systems, accounting and financial advice as well as engineering—all on the same basis of service rather than dictation.

Tremaine's temperament and abilities offset Terry's intense enthusiasm. His practical nature balanced Terry's idealism; his shrewdness in financial matters and his quietness of manner provided the needed foil for the crusading spirit he found in Terry. Together they made a formidable team as they set out to persuade other lampmakers throughout the country to join them.

Before long they confirmed the principal fear they had entertained about their proposal: it would take capital—a good deal more money than they could raise in their immediate circle of associates.

Several factory owners to whom they talked saw merit in the plan but felt that they would be giving up their business sovereignty if they accepted it. If so, they would rather sell their businesses to a new and larger company, if Terry and Tremaine wished to start one. They might be willing to run their manufacturing and sales activities as part of such a company. Terry could talk as much as he liked about the service arrangements he would set up in Cleveland, but they had their doubts. They had seen other examples of centralized control. Now if the two gentlemen had the capital to buy out the business . . . well then possibly a deal could be arranged.

Not all the manufacturers clung to this viewpoint. A few were willing to contribute, as affiliates, to the engineering organization in return for its obvious benefits. But it was clear that if a strong group were to be built, there would have to be funds to purchase quite a few existing companies.

Throughout their preliminary planning Terry and Tremaine had felt that their new organization must maintain friendly relations with General Electric. For one thing, General Electric held important patents on lamps and machinery. It would help the new group tremendously to have the right to utilize some of those patents. They knew something of Charles A. Coffin's business philosophy and believed that he might be favorable to their ideas.

Coffin believed very deeply in competition aimed at producing the highest possible quality of product throughout the industry. He applied this belief to the operations of various departments of General Electric. One G-E plant might be making a product that, in effect, competed with the product of another of the company's factories. Fine, said Coffin. Let the two organizations try to best each other. Each should keep improving quality; both products should be constantly tested competitively, just as though they were produced under separate ownership. The same spirit, he thought, should permeate the respective sales staffs and all other employee groups. Also, let competing companies (such as Sunbeam, Fostoria, and all the other lamp manufacturers) keep trying to improve quality of product and all phases of business operation. That would stimulate his own men to keep doing the same.

It was this broad-scale attitude that led Terry and Tremaine toward an unprecedented step in solving their main problem: they would ask General Electric to put up the money for their federation plan! Today this seems like a curious and quixotic idea. To top it off, Terry and Tremaine intended to withdraw from the new company if G.E. could be persuaded to provide capital. Both of them—Tremaine in particular—were interested in the possibilities of another infant industry, the manufacture of automobiles.

They felt that their plan would benefit the smaller lamp companies, but that General Electric would seek to control it in detail. Therefore, as soon as it was organized and operating, they would leave the lamp industry and go into the automobile business. Tremaine had already selected an automobile company and a location for this purpose.

ORGANIZATION OF THE NATIONAL ELECTRIC LAMP COMPANY

J. B. Crouse first approached Coffin on behalf of the Terry–Tremaine–Crouse group. Their preliminary conversation progressed favorably. Coffin approved the men sponsoring the plan. He had dealt with Crouse and H. A. Tremaine in their carbon business, and liked them.

Crouse arranged a second meeting in which Terry and B. G. Tremaine made a complete presentation. Coffin showed no hesitancy in accepting. General Electric would finance the formation of a new company. However, the G-E president astonished the others by insisting on two major conditions: (1) Tremaine and Terry must remain as the active managers of the new organization, and (2) they were to have complete management authority and responsibility, with General Electric taking no part whatever in operational control. In other words, G.E. would remain essentially a silent partner. One other requirement was that the new company would purchase and take over as its headquarters the Brush Electric Co. plant on East 45th Street in Cleveland, a General Electric property. Delighted by the free hand they were to have, Terry and Tremaine agreed to Coffin's terms just as readily as he had specified them. On May 3, 1901, they organized the National Electric Lamp Co. Capitalization was composed of $500,000 in common stock, $150,000 in preferred stock, and $2,000,000 in bonds. General Electric purchased 75 per cent of the common stock and held an option to buy the remainder.

Terry and Tremaine set out to form their federation of subsidiary companies and affiliates. To start with, of course, they had the Sunbeam and Fostoria companies. Within a few months they had added three companies that had been members of the Incandescent Lamp Manufacturers Association—Bryan-Marsh, Columbia, and Buckeye. Then they went on the road to sell others on enlisting under the National banner.

Their approach to the other lamp manufacturers had little appearance of high-pressure salesmanship. They called on the head of a company, asked how he was getting along, and discussed the problems of lamp production. They made no offers. After a while the company president grew restive. Usually he said: "Gentlemen, I think I know why you're here. It's not just to have a pleasant conversation about the lamp business. Aren't you going to make an offer to buy our company?"

"If you want to sell," was the reply, "we might very well be interested. But we are not urging you nor making any offers. It's entirely up to you."

In most cases the discussion then turned to a detailed offer of sale and the terms of purchase. Terry and Tremaine explained their proposed method of operation. This included the continued manufacture of the individual company's product (for example, Shelby lamps made by the Shelby Electric Co.) and usually the retention of the same management personnel as before.

In this way, during the years 1901–1906, the two men assembled the companies they wanted to affiliate with National. The preferred stock and the bonds of the new corporation were issued to the stockholders of the various individual companies in payment for their businesses. On several occasions Tremaine and Terry returned to General Electric for approval on expanding the capitalization to assure the purchase of desirable lamp companies. But one point that should be noted about this series of transactions was this: Aside from the top members of the National group and a few executives of G.E. and the Edison Lamp Works, no one knew of General Electric's financial interest in National.

By 1904 the National lamp system had become a well-rounded operation. In Cleveland the Development Laboratory and the Engineering Department offered research and testing services to the individual factories. In the same way, a Business Development section helped the member companies improve their marketing methods.

Representatives of the Engineering Department visited each factory once a month, with no advance notice. They selected lamps at random from the regular run and took them to Cleveland for testing. The factory managers received the test findings on all samples of lamps, but with only their own lamps identified as to results. The factory with the lowest average product-quality rating had to pay the largest share per lamp to support the Engineering Department operations. The others were also assessed according to the merits of their lamps. This naturally served as an incentive to improve each brand—and the lamps were still produced and marketed under their earlier brand names: Peerless, Packard, Colonial, Shelby, Sunbeam, Sterling, Banner, Fostoria, Buckeye, Bryan-Marsh, Columbia, and others.

More than 20 companies joined the federation at one time or another. In 1906 the name "National Electric Lamp Association" (Nela) was adopted for the entire group. (This was not the same as the National Electric Light Association, the members of which were principally electric-utility companies.)

With Terry and Tremaine as leaders, the National company soon became a potent force in the lamp business. The members of the Nela group held licenses under General Electric patents. After the formation of National's Engineering Department, the license agreements worked in both directions—that is, G.E. was entitled to licenses on National developments. And the skilled craftsmen in the new company began to contribute their share of the improvements in machines and methods. The result was a free exchange of technical information between General Electric and National.

The National group held frequent meetings in Cleveland during its first few years. The factory managers, sales managers, and other leaders discussed common problems and became better acquainted. They kept making progress in the quality and volume of their lamp production. Not only were their sales climbing, but they were also developing a spirit of cooperation and camaraderie unmatched anywhere else in the industry.

The plant on East 45th Street began to be uncomfortably crowded because of the growing business volume. National built additions and leased nearby buildings, but these too became inadequate. F. S. Terry, worrying over this problem, realized that the company would soon have to build new facilities. He did not favor a downtown Cleveland location, and he began to envision a new and different kind of site for the headquarters of the business.

The entire industry was taking shape as an important factor in American life. Millions more were becoming familiar with the convenience of electric light. As National grew, so did General Electric and Westinghouse. The lamp industry was booming—coming of age like a young man just turned 21.

CHAPTER 7

Research Develops
Strikingly Better Lamps

As THE WORLD turned into the twentieth century, a great sense
of anticipation and hope permeated the United States.
This was nowhere more apparent than in the realms of science and industry. The horseless carriage was beginning to become
an automobile. In hundreds of small workshops, set up with crude
equipment, mechanics and inventors were busy. They were experimenting with ideas that they hoped might develop into whole new
industries.

However, there was little industrial research along the lines familiar to us today. Development and testing laboratories, as such,
were few and far between. As for a genuine scientific laboratory
in industry, there was none. Such a laboratory would have pure
research as its prime function—without specific relation, in many
cases, to the development of a product.

American universities did not have adequate laboratories in this
sense, either. They were just beginning to see the possibilities, just
beginning to assemble the men and equipment, to start in a small
way the work for which they had previously looked to Europe.

At Lynn, Elihu Thomson directed General Electric's development laboratory. It was a good one, but it was concerned with
product development only—not the seeking of new principles in
the field of electricity. The company's illuminating-engineering
laboratory, established in Schenectady in 1899, dealt principally
with applications, such as street lighting and floodlighting.

Industrialists generally did not feel that research laboratories were within the scope of their business functions. They didn't even think of it. If anyone had suggested such an idea, almost all of them would have turned it down as a waste of money.

Nevertheless, in 1900 several leaders of General Electric, acting as a group, conceived the idea of establishing such a laboratory. No one of them alone can be credited with the initiative, and in later years they all shared it. Thomson was one of them. Another was E. W. Rice, vice-president and technical director of the company. The others were Charles P. Steinmetz, the consulting engineer, and A. G. Davis, manager of the Patent Department.

When these four discussed their suggestion informally with President Coffin, they received immediate support. Coffin with his broad vision was able to perceive the possibilities of the laboratory. He had confidence in his colleagues. He knew that nothing of the kind was available in the American academic world, and he saw no reason why General Electric should not try it.

So it was that in the fall of 1900 the first laboratory for fundamental research in American industry was established in Schenectady. The beginnings were humble enough. The first quarters for the laboratory were set up in a barn behind the house in which Steinmetz was living.

To take charge of the work, Rice hired a young man who was engaged in teaching and research work in chemistry at the Massachusetts Institute of Technology: Dr. Willis R. Whitney. Whitney was hesitant about accepting the position. He was occupied with interesting problems at M.I.T. and was naturally a bit skeptical about how much latitude he might find for basic scientific research in an industrial organization.

However, when Rice proposed a division of time between the company and the university, Whitney accepted. This arrangement remained in effect for three years. At the end of that time Whitney no longer doubted the value of the projects originated at Schenectady nor the working freedom that he and his staff would enjoy.

Laurence A. Hawkins has told the story of the General Electric Research Laboratory from 1900 to 1950 in his book, "Adventure into the Unknown." It is a definitive history and an intimate one because of Mr. Hawkins's many active years in various management capacities in the laboratory. Anyone interested in the accomplishments of the laboratory, ranging through many fascinating fields from lighting to metallurgy, electronics, and atomic power, should read the Hawkins book.

As Hawkins points out, it was Whitney who pioneered genuine scientific research in American industry. It was he who built and equipped the laboratory, selected and trained its staff, and provided incomparable leadership for more than 30 years.

At the start Whitney was the entire laboratory himself. The first of his assistants was J. T. H. Dempster, who had worked with Steinmetz earlier. In 1901 the laboratory was installed in a small frame building within the Schenectady Works. By 1904 Whitney's staff had grown to 12 persons; the personnel, the quarters, and the necessary equipment continued to grow steadily after that time. The early advisory council of the laboratory consisted of Rice, Whitney, Thomson, Steinmetz, Davis, and John W. Howell, engineer of the Edison Lamp Works. Others soon appointed to this group of advisors were John E. Randall, engineer of the National Lamp Works, and C. W. Stone and William Stanley, outstanding consulting engineers with the company.

SEARCHING FOR BETTER FILAMENTS

One of the first lines of investigation pursued by the laboratory was the basic examination of the nature of incandescent lamps and of the materials and processes that were used to make them, or might be used. The research laboratory was independent of the lamp end of the business or any other department. However, its facilities could be used to study any problem that might later affect any of the production departments.

The carbon-filament lamp had apparently reached the peak of its efficiency by the early 1900's. Up to that time Edison and others had improved its life and its light output, but by 1900 Edison was reported to believe that the incandescent lamp was not likely to be notably improved further.

Toward the close of the nineteenth century, experimenters in lamp design, especially in Europe, began to try to find ways to exceed the performance of carbon lamps by utilizing other filament materials. They were aided in this research by the development of the electric-arc furnace, which made it possible to get higher temperatures for studying the properties of metals and other chemical substances.

In 1897 Dr. Walther Nernst developed a new lamp with an initial efficiency of 5 lumens per watt (as compared with 3.4 lpw from the carbon lamp).

Nernst was a German professor of marked ability who was later (1920) to win the Nobel prize in chemistry. As the burner for his lamp he used various metallic oxides mixed together and formed into a tiny rod. Lane-Fox and Edison, among others, had suggested earlier the use of such materials as illuminants, but Nernst was the first to pursue work along these lines to a commercially useful conclusion.

The Nernst lamp, however, was awkward to handle, complicated, and expensive. A special heating coil of platinum wire had to be employed with it to preheat the metallic-oxide burner, which would not conduct electricity when cold. In spite of improvements made by others to whom Nernst assigned patent rights, his invention could not supplant the carbon lamp for most uses.

George Westinghouse purchased the American rights to the Nernst lamp patents. The lamp's efficiency gained it considerable sales, particularly in Europe, from 1902 through 1911. Other and more efficient lamps came on the market during those years, so before long the Nernst lamp ceased to be a factor in the business.

Among those more efficient lamps were further developments from central Europe. One was the osmium lamp, using the rare metal of that name for a filament. This was contrived by Carl von Welsbach, the Austrian who had invented the Welsbach mantle for gas lighting.

During his experiments from 1897 to 1900, Welsbach devised new methods of treatment so that the fragile metal could be formed into filaments (by squirting an osmium paste through dies). Initial efficiency was 5.5 lumens per watt. The rated lamp life was good: 1,000 hours. But again there were drawbacks: osmium was costly because of its rarity; it was brittle; very long filaments were necessary. Few customers were willing to pay $1 to $2 for the lamp. The American patent rights, applied for in 1898, were not approved until 1910. Therefore, the lamp was never manufactured commercially in the United States.

Technicians of the Siemens and Halske Company in Germany, profiting by the earlier research in metal filaments, developed the tantalum lamp during the period 1901–1903.

Tantalum, another metal that was in limited supply and very expensive, possessed advantages over osmium in workability. Again, long filaments (2 feet or more) were necessary. Initial light output of these lamps was 5 lumens per watt and life ranged up to about 800 hours.

First produced commercially in 1905, tantalum lamps were introduced to the United States market by General Electric and National in 1906. The two companies had purchased the American rights. For about six years the lamps were sold with some success, especially for use on direct-current circuits, where the lamp life was much more satisfactory than on alternating-current circuits. Alternating current caused the tantalum filament to crystallize rapidly, resulting in early failure. This factor, of course, placed a definite limit on the market for the lamps, since most of the current supplied in this country was alternating.

THE GEM LAMP

The foregoing discussion of the Nernst, osmium, and tantalum lamps is not detailed because the lamps themselves are not particularly interesting to the general reader. They show, however, the general stir of development in the lamp industry during the early years of the century, and point up the comparable work of the General Electric Research Laboratory during that time.

Throughout his long career Dr. Whitney has always possessed to the utmost degree a passion for basic experiment in attacking any scientific problem. Rather than accept an easy assumption that seems obvious, he insists firmly on beginning at the beginning. He would agree with another great scientist's maxim: the "obvious" is often incorrect.

Characteristically, then, his approach to the problem of lamp research was to examine the carbon lamp thoroughly and to say, in effect: "Let's see what we have here. How does it act? What are its strong points, and what are its weaknesses? Having examined those, we shall know what factors to study (or restudy) basically in chemistry and physics. We'll learn more about them and perhaps—who knows?—we may be able to improve lamp design as a result. This will not preclude the study of other possible filament materials besides carbon. It should in fact aid that study."

Of course this is not a unique attitude in science. But many others would have assumed that the carbon filament could not be further improved in any way, and that there was no point in studying the existing lamp before plunging into the search for other filament materials.

The bulbs blackened during their lives, and Dr. Whitney knew that this was an effect of evaporation of carbon from the filament. He believed that this darkening of the bulb might be due in considerable measure to the presence of certain ash oxides (such as silica) in the filament. These oxides could not be eliminated at the temperatures, and with the conditions, under which the filaments operated nor those under which they were normally treated by the "flashing" process. (The operating temperature up to that time was about $1700°C$. The highest treatment temperature used in the making of the filaments was about $2700°C$.)

What would happen—how would the filaments react—under higher temperatures? Whitney asked himself that question. In order to answer it, he had to construct a new type of electric-resistance furnace. In the highly heated carbon tube used in this furnace, he could get temperatures of about $3500°C$.

After heating a batch of filaments in his furnace, he used them in lamps and tested them. The results were surprisingly good. Several further tests, taking into account other factors, repeated the original success.

There were several beneficial results from the electric-furnace treatment. The ash oxides were reduced materially, as Whitney had anticipated. This lessened blackening of the bulb during the useful lamp life.

The operating temperature could be increased to about 1900°C, as compared to the previous 1700° level. The reason for this was that the treated coating of the filament—a graphite "shell" created by the high heat—became much harder and tougher as a result of the higher temperatures reached in the electric furnace.

The filament took on the characteristics of a metal filament: instead of lower electrical resistance occurring as operating temperatures were increased, there was higher resistance and therefore more light output.

Because of these changes in the filament characteristics, the lamp was called Gem (General Electric Metallized).

Gem lamps operated at 25 per cent higher efficiency than regular carbon lamps over the same useful life—600 hours. When designed for this rated life, the initial output of Gem lamps was 4.25 lumens per watt, compared to 3.4 lpw for carbon lamps. If the Gem lamp were operated at the same efficiency (light output) as the regular carbon lamp, it would last 4¾ times as long.

Dr. Whitney made his patent application on the Gem lamp in February, 1904, and the patent was granted in 1909. General Electric placed the lamps on the market in 1905 and sold them for the next 12 years.

Though the efficiency of these lamps was lower than that of the osmium, tantalum, and Nernst lamps, they were much easier to produce in quantity, easier to handle, and more durable than the others. Low cost was also an important factor. When introduced on the market the 20-candlepower Gem lamp sold for 25 cents, and this price was lowered as sales volume grew.

Beginning about 1905 the manufacturers changed lamp ratings from candlepower to wattage. A 50-watt carbon lamp was just about equivalent to the former 16-cp lamp. Because of its higher efficiency, a 20-cp Gem lamp also drew 50 watts and was so rated when the wattage basis was adopted.

THE TUNGSTEN LAMP

As the quest for new filament materials continued, the metal tungsten became a leading candidate. This was natural because of tungsten's very high melting point, about 3370°C, and because of its ready availability at rather low cost in the form of wolframite ore and other ores. Tungsten was known as one of the heaviest and hardest chemical elements. But these qualities still fell far short of guaranteeing that it would make good filaments for lamps.

Earlier experimenters found it intractable, either as a hard, brittle mass or an equally perverse fine crystalline powder that resisted being worked into a coherent form. Turner D. Bottome had tried to develop a combination tungsten and carbon filament in 1887 but was unable to come up with a practical solution to the problem. The Westinghouse company had retained Lodyguine, the Russian researcher, to attempt the development of a composite filament employing tungsten along with other materials, but his two years of work (1893–1894) had also been unsuccessful.

In Europe during the years 1902–1906 several leading research men were working diligently on tungsten filaments as well as other metals. The same was true to a lesser degree in the United States.

As it finally developed, the men whose tungsten lamp won primary recognition were Alexander Just and Franz Hanaman. They were laboratory assistants in chemistry in a technical high school in Vienna. Working from 1902 to 1904, they persisted until at last they had perfected a series of chemical processes resulting in a practical tungsten filament. Essentially this was a matter of combining tungsten with other materials in order to get a cohesive filament structure and then treating the mixture chemically and with heat. These processes removed the other materials, so that only tungsten of a substantially pure character remained and formed the filament.

In terms of efficiency the new product was sensational. The initial light output of these tungsten lamps was 7.85 lumens per watt, a tremendous advance over earlier lamps. In addition, the useful

Exterior of Edison's Menlo Park laboratory, the birthplace of the electrical industry, as it was restored at Greenfield Village, Dearborn, Mich.

Interior of the Edison laboratory, where he invented his incandescent lamp, as reconstructed. (*Photographs courtesy of Henry Ford Museum, Dearborn, Mich.*)

Miniature
Incandescent
Electric Lamps

For use with Batteries.

Instructive and Amusing for
the Boys.

Lamps of ½, 1, 2, 3, 4 or 6 candle power,
35 cents each.

**Miniature Candelabra and Decorative
· Lamps for use on electric light circuit.**

For Decorative Lighting in Residences these
Lamps are exceedingly effective.

Also Receptacles and Sockets.

X-Ray Tubes and Fluoroscopes.

Illustrated Catalogue, with Price-List, sent on application

Edison Decorative and Miniature Lamp Dept.
(GENERAL ELECTRIC CO.)

Fifth Street, Harrison, New Jersey

The first advertisement for General Electric
lamps, published in the *Saturday Evening Post*
of Feb. 4, 1899—an interesting contrast to the
colorful full-page G-E lamp advertisements of
the present day.

An early advertisement for Christmas-tree
lamps told the public about these amazing replacements for the candles that had been used
previously to light the tree.

ELECTRIC
LIGHTING OUTFIT

For
Christ-
mas
Tree
and House
Decoration

*Completely
made up
and ready for
use*

Retail price for complete outfit, including 28 one-candle
power miniature Edison lamps, neatly packed in handsome box, $12.00.   Liberal discounts to the trade.

MAIN SALES OFFICES

Edison General Electric Company
Harrison, N. J.

His Only Rival

Get cheaper electric light
from the Sun's Only Rival

General GE *Electric*
MAZDA LAMP

Order from your electric light
company or dealer, or write to

General Electric Co.-Schenectady, N.Y.

MAZDA lamps were advertised in this way in *Harper's Magazine*, May, 1910. Advertising like this helped to popularize the Edison lamp slogan: "The Sun's Only Rival."

Franklin S. Terry, one of the founders of the National Lamp Works. Terry originated new concepts of business management and was the leader in establishing Nela Park.

Burton G. Tremaine, who was also prominent in building the National Lamp organization. He worked side by side with Terry and later served many years as a director of General Electric.

William R. Burrows, an outstanding expert in factory operations. He functioned as general manager of the Edison Lamp Works and later as a vice-president of the General Electric Co.

George F. Morrison, another of the true pioneers in the lamp business. Morrison managed the Edison Lamp Works until 1916, when he went on to broader duties as a G-E vice-president.

Theodore W. Frech, who as general manager and vice-president guided the G-E Lamp Department through some of its most fruitful years.

Joseph E. Kewley, successor to Frech as a G-E vice-president, led the Lamp Department during the difficult depression years and during World War II.

lamp life was excellent—about 800 hours. The filaments were fragile, they were lengthy, and the lamps had to be very carefully handled. But the two laboratory workers, low-salaried and hard pressed for working facilities, had achieved one of the most notable triumphs in the history of lampmaking.

Just and Hanaman had to borrow the equivalent of $60 to pay for their applications for British and French patents in 1904, having exhausted their slim financial resources. Because they had no money, they were beaten to the punch by other European inventors in applying for United States patents.

One of these others was Dr. Werner von Bolton of the German company, Siemens and Halske. As the principal inventor of the tantalum lamp, von Bolton had worked out a theory for making filaments from other metals. These, he claimed, could be made ductile (capable of being drawn into the form of wire) just as tantalum was ductile by nature. His patent application claimed tungsten as one of these metals, but gave no description of any processing that would result in ductile tungsten.

Another claimant was Dr. Hans Kuzel of Vienna. He devised a system for making metal filaments, one of which was tungsten. The process was somewhat different from the method used by Just and Hanaman but resulted in filaments that closely resembled theirs.

Von Bolton made his American patent application on Nov. 10, 1904. Kuzel followed on Jan. 4, 1905, while Just and Hanaman filed on July 6, 1905.

In the meantime the Austrian Welsbach company had experimented further with the osmium lamp, using various other metals in combination with osmium. The Welsbach researchers found that the best combination consisted of osmium and tungsten. The resultant "osram" lamps were gradually changed, using less osmium and more tungsten, until finally they were entirely tungsten-filament lamps.

The situation regarding American patent rights was confused, to say the least. No one could say which inventor would be recognized as the originator of the tungsten lamp.

General Electric purchased an option on the Welsbach American rights for $100,000 in 1906 and began the manufacture of tungsten lamps the following year. The National company bought an interest in the rights from G.E. and also started making and selling the lamps. Engineers of both companies had to do considerable development work before the lamps could be manufactured in quantity. Even so, the American public was able to buy tungsten bulbs, more than twice as efficient as carbon, within a year after their introduction on the European market.

For full protection, the General Electric Company bought the American patent applications of Just and Hanaman in 1909 for $250,000; in the same year the company purchased Kuzel's application at a cost of $240,000.

After long deliberations in the Patent Office, the Just and Hanaman invention was approved and the patent granted, on Feb. 27, 1912. The Kuzel and von Bolton applications were turned down. Since von Bolton had not indicated a method for making tungsten ductile, his application was considered inadequate by the Patent Office, but the conflict between the other two applications boiled down essentially to a question of priority. Just and Hanaman had made their application for French and British patents with the borrowed money on Nov. 4, 1904; Kuzel had made application for an American patent on Jan. 4, 1905, just 60 days later. The difference between these dates was the main factor in establishing priority for Just and Hanaman. Their process was successful primarily on filaments for 40 watts and larger. For smaller-size tungsten lamps, Dr. Aladar Pacz of the National group developed a chemical process for making filaments of smaller size.

General Electric and National placed a price of $1.50 on the 40-watt tungsten lamp when it was introduced in 1907. The 60-watt lamp was priced at $1.75. Production costs were high and sales volume was low at first. During the next few years, however, prices dropped rapidly as production and sales increased.

The higher efficiency of tungsten lamps led to much better lighting, rather than to reductions in the revenues of central stations. As illumination grew better, utility-company income from lighting increased. Where the central-station companies had formerly replaced carbon lamps without charge (the "free renewal" system), most of them now charged customers for tungsten lamps. This had the effect of changing much of the distribution of lamps from the light and power companies to other channels, with this business going more and more to electrical wholesalers and dealers.

DUCTILE TUNGSTEN

Tungsten was still a stubborn metal. Just and Hanaman and the others, including General Electric research workers and engineers, had managed to fashion it into filament wires and so to make rather good lamps. Yet it was something like getting a fractious child to obey, halfheartedly and only part of the time, through the use of makeshift methods of discipline.

The metal was likely to break at any time, unable to survive rough handling, and was costly to fabricate. In its filament form it still presented many problems.

Even before the new lamps went on the market, the General Electric Research Laboratory had tackled the job of subduing tungsten further.

On Sept. 11, 1905, Dr. William D. Coolidge began work with the laboratory. This was a significant date because Coolidge, during the next 40 years, was to contribute some of the most fruitful research work the electrical industry ever saw. For 13 of those years (1932–1945) he was the laboratory's director, succeeding Dr. Whitney. He was assistant director from 1908 to 1928 and associate director for the next four years.

A graduate of Massachusetts Institute of Technology in electrical engineering, class of 1896, Coolidge took his doctorate in physics at the University of Leipzig, where Whitney had also earned his Ph.D. Again like Whitney, he joined the General Electric research staff after several years of teaching at M.I.T.

In 1906 Dr. Coolidge started work on the study and improvement of tungsten filaments. His first achievement in this field came with comparative ease in contrast to the adversities he was to encounter in later experiments.

He created an amalgam filament, using mercury, cadmium, and bismuth as a binder for powdered tungsten. Other materials had been used for the binder in earlier lamps. In both cases the entire mixture (of pasty consistency) was squirted through a die. Then the binder was removed by applying high heat and by passing a heavy current through the filament. This left a filament of rather pure tungsten. The treatment process, similar to that used for making osmium filaments, had the effect of sintering the tungsten —that is, partially fusing the tiny particles so that they would cling together better.

Coolidge's amalgam, originated in 1906, produced stronger and better filaments. It also made possible the manufacture of larger tungsten filaments for higher-wattage lamps.

Then he tackled the problem that had baffled so many experimenters in both Europe and the United States—metallurgists, physicists, chemists. How could tungsten be made ductile, so that it could be worked and drawn into a very fine, very tough wire, free of its maddening brittleness?

Like all such research projects in the laboratory, this was a group effort, in that Dr. Coolidge had helpers. The direction, however, was in his hands; the decisions were his, step by step.

Before developing the amalgam filament Coolidge had proved that the brittleness of tungsten did not derive from the presence of impurities but was a characteristic of the metal itself. He did this by making samples of tungsten as pure as he could make them and then deliberately adding impurities (other elements) and studying their effects. This saved the time and effort of trying to obtain superpure tungsten as a means of getting ductility. (It had been von Bolton's theory, based on his experience with tantalum, that a metal such as tungsten could be made ductile if the impurities were removed.)

For about two years of constant experiment, 1906–1908, Dr. Coolidge tried a variety of ways to treat tungsten.

He hammered it gently at various temperatures. These experiments showed some promise. The tungsten filaments treated in this way were elongated somewhat. But when allowed to cool they were still brittle.

He squeezed the filaments between the rolls of a small rolling mill such as jewelers used, with the rolls heated to about 300°C. Again the filaments lengthened under treatment. And again, discouragingly, they remained brittle when cool.

Next, Coolidge pressed tungsten between hot blocks of hardened alloy steel. From this he learned more about the reaction of the metal to hot working. The results gave a little more encouragement. Up to this point he had proved that tungsten filaments could be hammered, rolled, and pressed, with some gains in mechanical strength. Still the fact remained that this was not truly ductile tungsten.

Finally, Coolidge and his assistants drew a heated tungsten filament through tiny dies. The dies were also heated, and so were the pliers used to pull the filament through the dies.

This was a difficult process. It demanded painstaking effort and the utmost patience. Each die was smaller in diameter, by the merest trifle, than the last preceding die. For each draw, of course, the die opening was also a trifle smaller than the diameter of the filament to be drawn through it—*a fraction of* $\frac{1}{1,000}$ *inch* smaller. But, by keeping everything at rather high heat, Coolidge managed to complete the series of draws. And amazingly enough, the resultant tungsten wire had lost much of its brittleness. It had become both strong and pliable, even when cold! After more than two years of unremitting work, Dr. Coolidge had succeeded in producing ductile tungsten. The structure of the metal had been changed largely from crystalline to fibrous—and from brittle to tough. The structural change that made other metals fragile had made tungsten stronger.

This accomplishment, attained in the fall of 1908, was nevertheless only a good start. Laborious methods had produced a small amount of ductile tungsten in the laboratory, but that hardly solved the problem of turning out the material in quantity. It was not factory production, and any factory manager in the business would have scoffed at it as a lampmaking procedure. Many an invention dies at this same point—where the effort or expense of duplicating it makes mass production impractical.

The sample of ductile tungsten that Coolidge had developed was made from an original filament of pressed tungsten $\frac{25}{1,000}$ inch in diameter. Obviously, if commercial quantities of workable tungsten wire were to be manufactured, a much larger "ingot" or slug would have to be formed as the starting unit. Then it might be possible to draw a lengthy wire of the correct size for lamp filaments.

So Dr. Coolidge began trying to press tungsten powder into such a slug—¼ to ⅜ inch square in cross section and about 6 inches long. He tried molds of several different designs, and utilized several types of pressure, attempting to get a small but consistent body of tungsten.

After getting a fairly cohesive tungsten slug, he tried to harden it by means of various heat treatments. Time after time the result was disappointing; the slugs cracked to pieces whenever he tried to work them. A dozen ingenious methods resulted in repeated failures.

Dr. Coolidge would not give up. He next tried swaging machines. These machines had two small hammers (or die halves) that operated at high speed. Several hundred times a minute the rotating hammers gently struck the rod of tungsten which was fed through the machine. The hammers and the opening through which the rod passed constituted a swaging die.

Again, failure after failure occurred when existing swaging machines were used. (Such machines were used for working steel —for example, to hammer steel needles to a point.) So Dr. Coolidge, analyzing the reasons for failure, built special swaging dies and modified the machines. By using many successive dies, still keeping the tungsten hot during the swaging process, he was eventually able to reduce its diameter to 30 mils ($^{30}/_{1,000}$ inch). Of course the metal stock was elongated greatly during these operations. He now had ductile tungsten in a form small enough to be called a wire. It was too coarse for filaments, but now it could be drawn.

The final steps consisted of a great many draws of the heated wire through heated diamond dies. This processing reduced the wire to the sizes needed for filaments to suit various voltages and wattages.

Even after this successful creation of ductile-tungsten filaments in the laboratory, however, Dr. Coolidge had to solve other problems before the manufacturing operation could be transferred to the lamp factory. He overcame the annoying lack of uniformity in the tungsten ingots, which had caused failures with many of them.

Also, the very high heat of lamp operation tended to make the filament crystalline again. Tungsten crystals in the wire were often offset from each other in such a way that weaknesses developed and early failure of lamps occurred. So Coolidge had to find ways to reduce offsetting. The most effective method he found was to add a very small amount of thorium dioxide to the tungsten powder used in the formation of ingots. At long last the laboratory work was essentially finished. In March, 1910, General Electric announced Dr. Coolidge's success in making ductile tungsten. The further work in the laboratory through the remainder of 1910 and the early months of 1911 was concerned with perfecting processes rather than originating them.

The preceding account of Coolidge's work may seem lengthy but it really covers only the high spots (and some of the low ones) encountered in five years of concentrated effort. In succeeding years this work was to revolutionize lamp manufacture in many respects.

The list of advantages for lamps made with ductile tungsten filaments was long and impressive. First, filament strength increased tremendously: samples of drawn tungsten wire $\frac{1}{1,000}$ inch in diameter showed a tensile strength of more than 600,000 pounds per square inch. Lamps containing these filaments could take the shock and vibration of regular use in automobiles, railroad cars, and street railway cars. They could be burned in any position. (This was a real convenience. Earlier tungsten lamps usually had to be burned base-up.)

The filaments could be sized accurately for designed voltages and efficiencies. The wire could be coiled, in order to obtain concentrated sources of light for such focusing lamps as automobile headlights. Production costs were low compared to earlier tungsten filaments. Manufacturing was easier and more accurate, as methods were worked out to accomplish it, and the result was a much more uniform product.

The efficiency of the lamps climbed to 10 lumens per watt, with 1,000 hours of useful life. The long struggle in the laboratory was therefore proved worth while. So was the money expended in the laboratory on the project—more than $115,000.

Ductile-tungsten lamps came on the market in 1911—another product of General Electric research. The company scrapped a half-million dollars' worth of equipment for making squirted filaments, along with a half-million dollars' worth of squirted-filament lamps. In July, 1912, Dr. Coolidge applied for a final patent on the process for making ductile tungsten (having applied earlier for various parts of the procedure). The patent was granted Dec. 30, 1913.

The following prices applied to General Electric lamps made with the new filaments:

Prices of Ductile-tungsten Lamps

	15-WATT	25-WATT	40-WATT	60-WATT	100-WATT	150-WATT
March, 1912	.50	.50	.55	.75	1.10	1.65
October, 1912	.40	.40	.45	.60	.90	1.35

In terms of cost and effort in development and production, the change to ductile-tungsten lamps from carbon lamps was like the change the Ford Motor Company made from the Model T to the Model A. High first costs were necessary in order to give the public far better lighting. As costs declined over the years, price reductions followed regularly. More and more people were enjoying the benefits of the best lighting that research and manufacturing skill could produce.

OTHER RESEARCH DEVELOPMENTS, 1906–1912

Edison had used platinum lead-in wires for his lamps, and this precious metal continued in use for many years. It suited the purpose because, as a conductor of electricity, it could be readily joined to glass with a tight seal and had almost exactly the same coefficient of thermal expansion as glass. In other words, when heated it expanded at the same rate and to the same degree as glass; when cooled, it contracted just as glass did. Consequently, the use of platinum reduced the possibilities of cracks and air leaks that would cause lamp failure.

From 1900 to 1910 lamp manufacturers made attempts to replace some or all of the platinum in lead-in wires. It was expensive, as anyone knows who has purchased a platinum ring. But no other material existing in nature possessed the same attributes for lead-in wires. Most lamps made in the United States continued to use platinum, at least for the portion of the wires passing through the glass stem.

Byron E. Eldred, a New York consulting engineer, developed in 1911 the first substitute wire that was widely used. Eldred combined several materials—a core of nickel-iron, coatings of copper and silver, and an exterior covering of platinum. He applied for a patent on this wire in 1911 and sold rights to General Electric. The patent was granted in 1913.

The company's use of Eldred's invention continued for only about two years, however, because of a new development in the G-E Research Laboratory. In 1912 Dr. Colin G. Fink of the laboratory staff developed dumet wire. Dr. Fink had ably assisted Coolidge in the metalworking research that produced ductile tungsten. Now he invented a superior lead-in wire.

He dipped a nickel-iron wire core into copper sulphate to give it a thin copper coating. Then he inserted it in a brass sheath and a final outer sheath of copper. The layer of brass permitted brazing of the outer copper sheath to the nickel-iron core. The brazing was done in a furnace, where the brass melted and formed a joint between the other metals. The wire was called "dumet" (two metals) because both copper and nickel-iron were used.

The American patent Dr. Fink applied for in 1912 was finally granted in 1924. W. L. Van Keuren of General Electric added an improvement by coating the dumet wire with borax. When the wire was dipped into a borax solution, the resultant formation of copper borate made the wire more adherent to glass.

Dumet wire makes a very satisfactory tight seal for lamps—at least as effective as platinum and of course far less expensive. It has been used since 1913.

In 1909 and during the next few years there was also considerable activity in improving the "getters" used in manufacturing lamps. A getter is an active chemical agent used inside the bulb, either to obtain a better vacuum or to help prevent bulb blackening.

The Malignani process (discussed in Chapter 5) employed phosphorus to improve the vacuum. In that process, however, the phosphorus was not called a "getter." In 1909 John T. Marshall of General Electric devised a better method of getting a vacuum by dipping the filament and mount into phosphorus mixed with water. The lamps were exhausted and sealed off. Then, when the filament was burned for a short time at high incandescence, the phosphorus coating vaporized. The gases present in the bulb combined with the phosphorus and apparently settled on the interior glass wall of the bulb by a process of adsorption. In any event, the result was a good vacuum. Other getters, used later, had a similar effect.

Franz Skaupy, an Austrian chemist, pioneered the use of getters for another purpose: to reduce bulb blackening. The discoloration came from evaporated filament material deposited on the glass during the life of the lamp. Skaupy used chemical compounds of the halogen group, placed inside the lamp in the glass rod supporting the filament. The heat of normal operation caused the halogen compounds to break up chemically. They combined with the tungsten evaporating from the filament. This produced a deposit on the glass bulb that was lighter in color than the blackening in earlier bulbs. Skaupy obtained a U.S. patent in 1915, about five years after his original discovery.

Since the Skaupy getters were useful mainly in lamps of 100 watts or larger, General Electric carried on further research. Dr. Fink developed a getter for use with smaller bulbs: potassium iodide. Harry H. Needham of General Electric also experimented successfully in this field, the principal element in his getter being cryolite. The developments introduced by Fink and Needham were first utilized in 1912.

In later years a number of other improvements were made in the use of getters. Notable among these was the work of three men: Ernst Friederich, a German experimenter, and Frederic W. Gill and Harold Blake of General Electric.

MAZDA LAMPS AND MAZDA SERVICE

As the tungsten lamp began to replace the carbon lamp, the leaders of General Electric and National looked for ways to dramatize the research developments that were making their lamps better from year to year.

The research laboratory staff, growing rapidly, was making new discoveries. The engineers, such as John W. Howell and W. R. Burrows at Harrison and John E. Randall and T. W. Frech at Cleveland, were adding their contributions. Improved manufacturing methods matched the advances in lamp design. This research progress in all phases of lampmaking was giving customers more lighting value than ever before. The lamps incorporated the latest and best ideas in design and processing. A symbol was needed to designate these facts to the public.

In 1909 General Electric and National jointly adopted the trade-mark MAZDA for certain of their lamps. This was not the name of a product but the mark of a service. The brand names previously used were continued. For example, bulbs manufactured at Harrison had been sold as Edison lamps. Now they were called Edison MAZDA lamps. The word MAZDA symbolized the research, the testing, and the manufacturing techniques that combined to make the lamps superior.

In Persian mythology, the god of light was known as Ahura Mazda. To the Persians, light was synonymous with knowledge and goodness, and so was the name Mazda.

Much deliberation and debate preceded the choice of this peculiarly fitting name. At one of the annual meetings of managers a prize contest was held among the men to select a suitable name. However, in the discussions that followed there was some opposition to the prize-winning name and it was not adopted.

Some time later, at a meeting of top executives and others interested in the lamp business, the subject came up again. Among the men in the group were F. S. Terry, A. G. Davis, and Frederick P. Fish. Around the conference table they concentrated on finding the elusive word or phrase that would serve their purpose. Suddenly Fish broke the silence.

"MAZDA," he said. "That's the name! Let's call them MAZDA lamps, after the ancient god of light."

More discussion followed, but finally the group agreed. Fish was a leading patent lawyer of the time, retained as a counsel by General Electric. He made many important contributions to the business by his work in the complex field of patent law, but it is doubtful if any of them meant more in the years that followed than his suggestion of the MAZDA trade-mark.

Both General Electric and National began to use the mark on lamps using ductile-tungsten filaments. But the application of the name was only a small part of the MAZDA development. The most significant element was the research and test procedure standing behind the name. It came to be known as MAZDA service, and for many years it provided an assurance of the highest lamp quality.

The way to check on lamp quality is to test the lamps—constantly and rigorously. Tests of lamp life, of lamp strength, of all essential characteristics—these tell the factory manager and the laboratory researcher how good the lamps are and point toward possible ways to make them better.

The testing procedures that had been carried on in the various lamp plants and laboratories were now enlarged and intensified. For several years the General Electric Research Laboratory carried on most of the MAZDA service testing. Later (starting in 1920) the testing was handled by the Electrical Testing Laboratories, an independent organization in New York City.

Laurence A. Hawkins, executive engineer of the research laboratory, and Benjamin F. Fisher of the laboratory staff were the key men in establishing and maintaining the MAZDA service system of lamp testing and quality inspection. Hawkins had joined the laboratory in 1903. Fisher, after some years with Westinghouse, joined General Electric about the time MAZDA service was started. Under their supervision, the system steadily grew into a dynamic means of progress in making better and better lamps.

One of their toughest problems in the early years was winning the cooperation of factory managers in setting up an independent inspection service, not only at Schenectady but in every General Electric and National lamp plant.

A manager naturally felt that he knew best how to maintain quality, how to spot errors in manufacture that might result in defective lamps—in other words, how to run his business. He was not happy about the proposal to place an inspection team in his factory to take random samples of his finished production and subject them to inspections and tests in addition to those he would normally make.

Gradually, however, Fisher and Hawkins and their staff proved the advantages of such a system. There were not only advantages to the public in maintenance of high quality, and benefits to the companies, but there were also very definite advantages to the factory managers and employees.

The product of every lamp plant was in competition with the other factories in the MAZDA service system. Samples of the finished products were thoroughly tested in a completely impartial manner, and the results were reported regularly to the managers. They could see exactly where they stood on the quality scale. They could be sure that the testing in all the plants had been strictly comparable. In addition, they found in this system better opportunities to remedy any processing that might be causing faulty production. The idea was not to run a manager's business nor to tell him what to do, but to give him facts about his product upon which he could base his planning and action for further improvement. Before long the inspection service was wholeheartedly accepted by the managers.

MAZDA service also brought to each factory the latest approved design ideas and manufacturing improvements. A change might be proved beneficial either in the research laboratory, in one of the development laboratories, or in a factory. Once an idea had been thoroughly investigated and accepted, a standardized procedure was set up to carry it to every plant and place it in universal operation.

The farsighted investment in research exemplified in the General Electric Research Laboratory was now bearing fruit. Essentially the carbon-lamp era was over, though the change to tungsten lamps was gradual and carbon lamps were still manufactured. Hardly a week passed without some small but significant improvement in lamp design or manufacture. Modern science had largely replaced cut-and-try methods in the industry.

CHAPTER 8

Great Changes in the Industry Picture

THE DUCTILE-TUNGSTEN LAMP opened tremendous new opportunities for growth in the lighting industry. And the lamp business did grow at a rapidly accelerating pace. In 1909 the production of large lamps totaled 66.7 million; this was the output of all U.S. manufacturers. (Large lamps include the standard line of bulbs most commonly used, and form a classification distinct from miniature lamps such as flashlight bulbs, indicator lights, etc.) Ten years earlier the figure for large lamps had been 25.3 million. By 1914 production had reached 88.5 million, a gain of more than 32 per cent in five years.

In 1909 only 20 per cent of large lamps had tungsten filaments; the great majority were still carbon lamps. By 1914 about 85 per cent were tungsten lamps.

General Electric's Edison Lamp Works continued to progress under the leadership of George F. Morrison, with Howell and Burrows the chief technicians and Almon D. Page as sales manager. Morrison had joined the organization in 1882 and had been general foreman and superintendent before attaining the position of works manager. Page, known to everyone in the industry as "Adam" rather than Almon, had entered the Edison Works as assistant factory manager and sales manager in 1890. After 1892 he concentrated his talents on sales.

The General Electric operation had already matured considerably by the turn of the century. It was in the National Electric Lamp Association that the most noticeable changes occurred in lamp-industry organization between 1900 and 1910. In Cleveland

and the many associated lamp factories throughout the country, there was effervescent activity everywhere. Terry acted as vice-president and general manager of the parent company, with B. G. Tremaine the second vice-president and sales manager. They were building a solid, efficient business structure. The other officers played prominent parts in this effort: J. B. Crouse, president; H. A. Tremaine, treasurer; and J. Robert Crouse, secretary. Their task was made much easier by the capable men they had brought into the National group.

TYPICAL NATIONAL MEN

It would be futile here to attempt a summary of all the notable individual achievements by those who pioneered the development of the National company. However, a few leaders so typified the company's spirit and the abilities of its men that they can be singled out as examples.

For instance, there were John E. Randall and T. W. Frech, Jr., who worked together on so many projects that they came to be considered as a team. These two men combined expert laboratory knowledge with all the skills needed to design and manage lamp factories. Randall had the same type of ingenuity in lampmaking as his opposite number at Harrison, John Howell. He started with Thomson-Houston at Lynn in 1886 as an electrician. By 1895 he had transferred to the Columbia company in St. Louis and advanced to the position of factory superintendent. In 1903 he became filament and lamp engineer of the National group. With Frech, he planned, organized, and operated National's first tungsten-lamp factory. Randall's facility in all phases of lamp development and production was accompanied by a genial, easy-to-work-with nature that inspired his associates.

Theodore W. Frech began his lamp-manufacturing career as an assistant to F. S. Terry in 1901. During the next three years, Terry sent him to work in several lamp factories: Fostoria, Bryan-Marsh in Marlboro, Mass., the Columbia plant in St. Louis, and others. Young Frech handled these special assignments exceptionally well. So in 1904 Terry brought him into the Cleveland headquarters.

For the next nine years he held several responsible positions, including the management of the East 45th Street Works. Gentle and quiet, Frech was a remarkable "idea man," never at a loss for new projects on which he lavished intense interest and enthusiasm. He worked on the development of the tantalum lamp, the pressed tungsten filament, and the drawn-wire tungsten filament. It was the activities of Frech and Randall that grew into the Lamp Development Laboratory of National. Randall managed the laboratory from its formal inception in 1909 until 1914, when he became the company's consulting engineer.

The Engineering Department, of course, formed the nucleus around which the National factories were combined into a strong federation. Terry and Tremaine found in Samuel E. Doane the man to manage this work and assemble a competent staff. They brought him to Cleveland in 1900 from the Bryan-Marsh company in Marlboro, where he had been superintendent for three years, but his lampmaking experience started some years before that.

Beginning in 1886, Doane was an engineer and assistant foreman of the Thomson-Houston incandescent-lamp factory. He moved to the Edison Works in 1892 when General Electric concentrated its lamp manufacturing at Harrison. First as an assistant engineer and later as superintendent, he earned the reputation that led to his Bryan-Marsh appointment and the position as chief engineer of National. As he built his department at Cleveland, several key assistants helped to establish National's engineering prestige. Notable among these men were Ward Harrison and W. M. Skiff—Harrison as a brilliant engineer and Skiff as the staff director who relieved Doane of many management responsibilities.

Doane inaugurated a constructive program of activities that profoundly affected the progress of the whole lighting industry. Among these were the development of basic knowledge of lighting requirements in many specific fields; the design of lighting systems; and the publication of the pioneer bulletins on lamps and lighting. Doane was a leader in planning the use of light on a sound economic basis, in the standardization of bases and sockets, and in the simplification of product lines to improve quality and lower the costs to the consumer.

As National grew, there was no lack of factory managers capable of competing with the best talent anywhere else in the industry. There was William H. Roberts, whose diversified background with many lamp companies from 1891 to 1906 prepared him for assuming the managership of manufacturing for National in 1909. He led that department for 16 years. There was Philip J. Pritchard, Roberts's first lieutenant, who was to cap a distinguished career with his direction of the pilot-plant work on fluorescent lamps many years later. A dozen more could be named from the National team. Characteristically they had climbed through the ranks in several companies. Now they cooperated in the National group while at the same time vigorously trying to outdo each other in improving filaments, machinery, glass, and lamp-assembly operations.

Good machine designers were most essential to progress in making better lamps. Here, too, National was well represented. John T. Fagan and his associates in the machine shops matched the work of the experts in the Edison Lamp Works in developing lampmaking machinery. In fact, the researcher today finds it impossible to establish clear-cut priorities in this field. Did a certain improvement in the sealing-in machine or in stem-making come first from Harrison or from Cleveland? Often the answer is that the machine designers in both organizations hit upon the better method at practically the same time. They "borrowed" each other's ideas whenever they could. If one factory got a step ahead, it wasn't long before the mechanics in another plant had "improved the improvement."

National's excellent developments in the manufacture of lamp glass were centered in the Fostoria Glass Works, led by Edward O. Cross.

On the scientific side, National established the Nela Research Laboratory in 1908, with Dr. Edward B. Hyde, an able physicist, as director, aided by Dr. Herbert E. Ives and Dr. Percy W. Cobb. Within the next six years the laboratory staff grew to include seven physicists, a physiologist, a psychologist, and a considerable number of assistants. They studied the production of light and the effects of light on human welfare. It was no longer merely a matter of making and selling bulbs; the industry was beginning to study the basic scientific aspects of lighting applications.

ASSOCIATION ISLAND

The meetings of National Electric Lamp Association managers grew into a unique institution as the years passed. In 1904 Terry and Tremaine decided that an annual summer get-together should be held at some attractive location away from Cleveland, so that business and pleasure could be combined. In that year the meeting took place in Muskoka, Ontario; in 1905 at Montmorency Falls, Quebec; and in 1906 at Chautauqua, N.Y. These were all delightful resort locations. However, the National leaders were not satisfied until they had found a permanent gathering place.

They found what they wanted in 1907—a sizable island in Lake Ontario about 2 miles offshore from Henderson Harbor, N.Y. Terry, Tremaine, and a few associates purchased the island, christened it Association Island, and arranged for the building of necessary facilities. The first Association Island meeting or "camp" was held in the summer of 1907.

During succeeding years the Island's buildings and equipment were greatly expanded. They included an administration building with a general store and post office, quarters for permanent caretaking personnel, a theater, boathouses, and landing docks. Large tents with wooden floors served as sleeping quarters for all those attending Island camps. The sports facilities included fishing, boating, swimming, golf, tennis, baseball, bowling, trapshooting—in fact, almost any game or sport desired.

There was a very definite purpose behind the plans for the Island's use. Terry and Tremaine had stated their policy of operation in these words: "National is not to be an organization of people working for other people; it is to be an organization of people working together, at many different tasks, for the ideals and public service of the organization as a whole." The Island provided a concrete means of demonstrating this policy and making it work.

The men attending the Island camps were, in many cases, former business rivals. Even after joining National, they competed with each other for business. Each wanted to make his particular brand of lamps better (Sunbeam, Bryan-Marsh, etc.) and wanted to sell more of them. Disagreements and misunderstandings were bound to arise. There were the usual possibilities of petty jealousies over promotions and of friction between men working in the same department.

Tremaine and Terry believed that when men not only worked together, but relaxed together at an Island camp, they would build mutual respect and liking that could come about in no other way. The meetings on the Island covered common problems and allowed for serious business planning.

Each meeting set up an organization with a camp manager and a staff of assistants, athletic directors, and committees to handle a dozen different activities. A "show" committee planned and presented a comedy burlesquing the rigors of the lamp business they had encountered during the year. During this entertainment the "bosses" received a good-natured roasting—as thorough as the drubbing administered to national political figures at the annual Gridiron dinners in Washington.

In 1909 the men at camp organized the Society of Nela, with an elaborate constitution and bylaws. There were three classes of members: the Graybeards, who were the original members; first-year men making their first trip to camp; and second-year men who had been initiated but hadn't yet graduated to the august and privileged rank of Graybeard.

Working as they did in many different parts of the country, the men got to know each other more thoroughly at these Island meetings than they could have done at formal business meetings. The ability of a newcomer to the Island to "take it" when initiated into the Society of Nela indicated as much about his character as his daily actions in business—perhaps more. Then, besides group activities, there were countless opportunities for two men to talk calmly together about mutual problems or disagreements.

Association Island was fully shared by the Edison Lamp Works people, too, starting in 1909. They held regular meetings on the Island and helped to expand its facilities just as the National group did.

The days at the Island comprise some of the happiest memories of many men still in the lamp business. They say: "We got rid of more gripes, inhibitions, and misunderstandings on the Island than we ever did any other way."

1911 ANTITRUST SUIT

As stated previously, few of the people associated with National or the Edison Lamp Works knew of General Electric's financial interest in the National company. Terry, Tremaine, and the other National officers exercised complete control over their operations, with no interference by the G-E officials. Cross-licensing agreements gave each company the use of the other's findings in research and development. But they competed keenly in the application of those findings and they contested with each other for lamp business in the expanding market.

During the administration of Theodore Roosevelt the Department of Justice embarked on a vigorous antitrust program. This continued after the election of William Howard Taft in 1908, and suits were filed in a wide variety of industries. One of these was directed at the incandescent-lamp business. On March 3, 1911, the Justice Department brought suit in the U.S. Circuit Court of Northern Ohio against General Electric and 34 other companies. These included National and its subsidiaries, Westinghouse, the Corning Glass Works, and several other glass and machine manufacturers.

In June of the same year General Electric filed answers to the government charges. Later, however, the company, on advice of its counsel, decided to accept a decree. The presiding judge, John M. Killitts, handed down a decree on Oct. 12, 1911. It applied to the other companies as well as to G.E.

The Court directed General Electric to operate the National company and its subsidiaries as an integral part of the G-E business. This was by far the most important provision. By this time National's percentage of the total lamp business in the United States closely approached that of the Edison Lamp Works; both ran far ahead of their nearest competitor.

The decree ruled out any direct price agreements between the lamp manufacturers. However, a patent owner could specify prices and terms of sale on patented lamps made by a licensee. This applied to the sales of manufacturing licensees; fixing of resale prices was disapproved. Finally, the decree prohibited certain limitations from being included in agreements made by the lamp companies with suppliers of glass, machinery, and other materials.

In compliance with the decree, General Electric purchased the remaining 25 per cent of the National common stock. The National company became the National Quality Lamp Works of General Electric (later shortened to National Lamp Works of G.E.). Terry and Tremaine remained as managers, assured by General Electric's top officers that they would have a free hand in operating their part of the lamp business.

The whole industry had to review its operations and devise new plans in 1912. There was a great opportunity to bring increasing lighting benefits to the American public—to lead the way with light. This was the prime objective of the new plans worked out by the industry's leaders.

PART THREE

Leading the Way with Light

CHAPTER 9

Nela Park—the University of Light

SOME TIME before the 1911 antitrust suit, F. S. Terry took action to end the frustrations caused by National's cramped and crowded quarters in Cleveland. Terry dreamed of a future location entirely different from the typical industrial environment. Quietly he began to investigate outlying areas, far from the busy midtown sections. He could imagine a spacious headquarters site, with acres of well-kept ground, plenty of room for expansion, and no air pollution or distracting noise.

They could have attractive buildings, he reasoned, something better than the monotonous, ugly construction that had always been used for factories and for most office buildings. Each building could be planned for the special needs of the department it would house.

Since that time hundreds of industrial organizations have recognized these and similar advantages. The trend today is toward outlying locations. But in 1910 such an idea was decidedly a novelty.

When Terry first described his plan to his associates, they treated it with cool reserve. He was so persistent, though, that he finally persuaded them to go on an inspection tour of several possible sites. They drove through the outskirts of Cleveland and finally stopped at the location Terry preferred. As the manager expounded the benefits of his scheme, his companions grew more and more incredulous.

"But this is 'way out in the country," they said. "It might be all right for a farm or a residential area or even a college campus. But it doesn't have any of the facilities needed for a business."

Terry marshaled his selling points:

1. Lower land costs and construction costs than a tall downtown building or series of buildings would require.

2. Lower taxes and operating costs.

3. Better atmosphere for effective work—much more pleasant working conditions.

4. Every building designed for its specific uses.

5. The fact that employees could also live in the neighborhood, in less expensive, more enjoyable homes than they would otherwise have, and within easy travel distance to and from their work.

6. Public attention and interest, stemming from the novelty of the idea, yet not conflicting with the solid advantages that National would realize.

"We'll have ample room to expand," he said. "The business is going to grow beyond anything we've seen yet. Why place ourselves where we'll be overcrowded again in another ten years? Why can't a business place be beautiful as well as useful? We'll all feel better, work better, live better. We'll be happier all around."

The others remained skeptical and for several weeks nothing further was decided on the subject. Finally, however, Terry won acceptance from Tremaine and the others, and their own imaginations began to catch fire. In September, 1910, they agreed on the selection of the site and started working out detailed plans. The land needed initially—33 acres—was purchased in January, 1912. They chose the name Nela Park for the future home of the National Lamp Works, with Nela being derived from the initials of the National Electric Lamp Association.

It was truly handsome acreage, rising southward above the intersection of Euclid Avenue and Noble Road in East Cleveland. Most of the land was at the top of the hill, where it flattened out at an elevation 230 feet above the level of Lake Erie. Toward the east it sloped away again into a series of wooded ravines that added immeasurably to the natural beauty of the scene.

BUILDING A NEW HOME

The National management wanted to make Nela Park really different from the average commercial enterprise. The buildings, they felt, should harmonize with the surroundings.

As the chief architect for the project they chose Frank E. Wallis of New York City. Frank Goodwillie, an architectural engineer, served as his top assistant. The National officials brought the architects to Cleveland to "live with them" for several months. By drawing their plans at the East 45th Street plant, they were better able to assess the needs of each department.

A modified Georgian style was selected for the buildings, and Wallis spent some time in England for further study of the eighteenth-century architecture he was to adapt for Nela Park. The structural supports of the buildings consisted of steel and reinforced concrete, resting on stone foundations. The exteriors were of brick, together with contrasting terra cotta. These materials were chosen with great care, and the brickwork and stonework planned to the last detail for pleasing appearance as well as utility. The simple lines sketched by the architects avoided any effect of massiveness or overdecoration.

Planning went ahead during the antitrust suit even though there was naturally much uncertainty about the future. The cornerstone for the Engineering building was laid on March 25, 1912, about five months after the G.E.—National combination resulting from the suit. This building stood on the north side of the broad main quadrangle.

Construction of the Nela Research Laboratory began in April. In late July the workmen started erecting the Sales building (later known as Sales Promotion and now the Advertising building) on the east side of the quadrangle. Meantime work had been progressing on the Nela Operating building, to serve as the maintenance headquarters for the entire plant. Located near the Noble Road entrance, this was the first structure to be completed. At the south side of the main square, the largest of the original group of buildings began to take shape. This was the Lamp Development

Laboratory, where the experimental work on products, the testing of lamps, and similar activities would be carried on. Beyond the Sales building and a short distance away from the quadrangle was the Administration building, containing the top-management offices.

The fourth structure facing the grassy central plaza, at the west end, was not erected until the others were occupied. It later became the best-known building of all because it was to house the famous G-E Lighting Institute, visited annually by thousands of people eager to see and study the latest developments in lamps and lighting. On the quadrangle side of the Institute the builders constructed a million-gallon water pool 120 feet in diameter. This was originally intended as a storage tank for Nela Park's water supply, but the architects left it open at the top and made it a decorative element rather than an eyesore. Later the water supply was otherwise provided and the pool remained as a pleasant feature of the landscape, beautifully lighted at night.

Also notable in later construction was an entrance lodge at the foot of the hill, approached by a street cut through from Euclid Avenue and called Nela Avenue. From this a winding drive climbed the hill to the Engineering building and continued beyond to join the other driveways through Nela Park—a total of more than 4 miles of paved roadway.

Power and heat came from a central power plant, with wires and pipes placed underground in an ingenious arrangement of tunnels. The tunnels ran mostly under the sidewalks between buildings and the heat loss from the pipes helped to keep the walks clear of snow in the winter.

Moving day for the National Lamp Works came on April 18, 1913. It was a big day in many ways. First, there was the diversity of people involved in the move: factory workers handling many different jobs, engineers, clerks, metallurgists, executives, salesmen, stenographers, physicists, maintenance men, chemists—now they all had the opportunity to settle down in spacious buildings designed for comfort and efficiency. The physical task of moving this business headquarters has of course been surpassed since 1913 but it had very seldom been equaled before that time. Finally the

200 moving vans made their last trip to Nela Park, completing the transfer of some 18,000 boxes and crates plus an enormous tonnage of other equipment.

LIVING IN THE NEW HOME

It took many more years, naturally, before Nela Park evolved into the greatly expanded headquarters it is today. The total area is now 85 acres. Other buildings added from time to time brought the total to more than 20. Gradually the landscaping was perfected, so that the site came to resemble a well-manicured university campus.

Employee health and comfort received painstaking attention from the start. Additions to this program comprised an impressive list: a cafeteria and dining room serving good meals at cost; rest and recreation rooms for women; a well-stocked general library for employees; a dispensary providing medical, dental, and nursing care; a barber shop; a transportation office; a large garage and parking area; and a branch bank of the Cleveland Trust Co.

The recreational facilities established over the years would make a chapter in themselves. They included tennis courts, baseball diamonds, an outdoor swimming pool, and bowling alleys. Some distance removed from the main buildings, several acres were transformed into Nela Camp, with many features comparable to those on Association Island. An auditorium, a kitchen, accommodations for indoor or outdoor dining, and a variety of sports fields made ample summer recreation available to employees. Beyond that, they provided for business meetings that could be relaxed and undisturbed, with plenty of fun to follow the serious thinking.

These are some of the resources of present-day Nela Park, enumerated here to give a preview of the fulfillment of Franklin S. Terry's hopes and dreams.

Terry lived with his job. During the earlier years he resided in a small frame house directly opposite the East 45th Street office building. At Nela Park he combined his home and his office, maintaining an apartment on the top floor of the Administration building. Here he could keep in constant contact with the business and with his friends throughout the company. Fastidious in dress, fond of order and careful detail, Terry followed a strict personal regimen. One of his favorite forms of relaxation was to walk through the tree-covered ravine behind the building where he lived. On these walks he liked to be accompanied by one or another of his colleagues. Then they could discuss and settle problems away from office routine and on a basis of friendship rather than brass-hat commands. His main interests in the lamp business were research, education, and more freedom and responsibility for employees, since he thought that freedom of action and the responsibility for the action went hand in hand.

B. G. Tremaine maintained a lively interest in half a dozen other industrial fields. Financial management was his forte. When Terry and others presented a major suggestion in a management meeting, Tremaine usually sat quietly listening to the enthusiastic "idea selling." Often there were alternative proposals vigorously backed by their sponsors. At a suitable moment Tremaine pinpointed the most pertinent factors involved in reaching a decision. With one or two questions he helped the group reach the most practical solution.

Chief among his projects outside the lamp business was the operation of the Peerless Motor Car Co., in which he and other National officers held a considerable financial interest. H. A. Tremaine left National in November, 1912, to become treasurer of Peerless. The Crouses also soon centered their activity in the Peerless operation, with J. B. Crouse becoming a vice-president of the automobile firm. J. Robert Crouse served as National's sales manager from 1912 until his resignation in 1916. T. W. Frech was also an active manager of Peerless for several years before returning to the lamp business.

As a result of these changes the management of the National Lamp Works was left almost entirely to F. S. Terry and B. G. Tremaine from the time the business was established in its new headquarters.

Meanwhile a whole new generation of capable men was growing up in the business. Terry and Tremaine were quick to recognize that the pioneers in lampmaking must be succeeded by younger men even better trained than the "Old Guard." The transition should be planned, not haphazard. They looked to the colleges and universities for new talent.

Early in the National company's development they set up an Employment Committee for the selection of outstanding graduates who would adopt the lamp business as a career. The committee included executives in sales, engineering, and manufacturing. The result was a steady influx of promising newcomers, particularly notable in 1909 and 1910. In each of these years more than 50 such young men entered the company. The same was true of the Edison Lamp Works at Harrison. It has been most interesting to see how many managers and key men in the General Electric Lamp Division came from this farsighted manpower-building program.

The National management organized two companies in 1911 to operate an investment and profit-sharing plan for department managers and other key employees. The original capital stock of these investment funds totaled more than half a million dollars. Profit-sharing was not confined to Nela Park personnel, but extended to sales, service, and manufacturing people throughout the country, who were accomplishing so much to maintain the company's position. For many years the profit-sharing plan supplied an unequaled incentive toward initiative, responsibility, and plain hard work to improve the lamp business and the welfare of every employee.

Nela Park gained nationwide recognition as a remarkable new venture in American industry. In 1913 the National Lamp Works won the top award for service to employees, given by the International Exposition of Safety and Sanitation. In 1920 Nela Park was selected as "the best-kept plant in America" in a contest sponsored by a leading business magazine. Among the many elaborate entries submitted, the judges could find nothing in American industry to equal it.

Even the value of Nela Park as a working place came to be

transcended by its educational value in the field of lamps and lighting. For employees throughout the country, for people from electric-utility companies, for wholesalers and retailers of lighting equipment, and for the general public it became known as the most prolific source of lighting information—truly a "university of light."

CHAPTER 10

A New System of Business Management

PEOPLE WORKING together for the benefit of all. By now that's a cliché—but what a wonderful idea when it's expressed in action! The New England town meeting is one example. There are dozens of others, such as the Red Cross, the Community Chest, or any organization that practices the idealistic principles it preaches.

Many businesses also employ this well-worn phrase. But whether the group concerned is a welfare society, a church, or a business, lip service to the ideal is not enough. To mean anything it must be manifested in deeds and in beneficial results. And that's not easy.

The management of the National Lamp Works believed in this ideal. Furthermore, they realized that it could not be fulfilled in any business organization unless it was so blueprinted that the lines of constructive action would be clear to everyone involved. Simply saying "Let's all work together" wouldn't do it. So they formulated the basic principles and policies they believed essential to successful business operation.

The result was a new system of business management, quite different from the usual "line" type of organization.

THE LINE ORGANIZATION

The line system consists of a chain of command. Orders come from the top, filter through various levels, and so are carried out. Often, in order to get decisions on even minor questions, they must be passed in reverse order through much of the same chain of command.

It was largely because the line type of operation originated in the military that Terry and his associates disapproved it. "Warfare," they said, "is destructive and inefficient; business cannot afford to be."

They also noted that the following deficiencies are typical of the line organizations in business:

1. Development of new talent or new methods is not as effective as it should be, because the top leaders cannot have enough contact with individuals. They must depend on recommendations coming through a long chain. Many good suggestions are lost or blocked on the way.

2. The tendency is to promote individuals because they are "next in line" rather than on the basis of fitness for the work.

3. Delays and red tape often result from the worker's inability to act without referring minor matters to superiors in the chain of command.

4. There is too much emphasis on winning grandiose titles, pleasing the boss, and building a complicated hierarchy of officials. These objectives take precedence over the only true measurement of a worker's ability or the value of a department: accomplishing truly useful and satisfactory results on the job.

5. Foremen and department managers are charged with *responsibility* for their operations but do not receive comparable *authority* to fulfill the requirements of their jobs.

6. To sum up, there is too little opportunity to develop individual initiative and skill. The training of people to take on better jobs and more responsibility may bog down as a result.

The objections of the National management to the line system of company formation have carried over for many years in the history of the G-E Lamp Division. Some years ago a factory manager in the Lamp Division discussed this with an interviewer. He talked about the thinking that led to adoption of another organizational method.

"It's hard to explain," he said, "but we feel we have a different way of considering our common goals and evaluating the people working with us.

"We regard the worker in business, at any and all levels, as a responsible and responsive individual. That man or woman has some qualities of initiative and dependability. They're not always apparent, to be sure. And if he doesn't have these normal human traits, it will usually show up pretty quickly. He can't make the grade and isn't worth keeping as an employee.

"Usually, though, even if he's just an average American with average talents, he has pride in his work. He holds a democratic belief in equal opportunity according to ability. He doesn't enjoy just going through the motions in order to keep his job. He doesn't mind taking orders from a boss he respects, but he wants to do more than take orders all the time. He wants some responsibility and the authority to carry it out—not selfishly, at the expense of others, but in line with his own capacities.

"That's the attitude that builds leaders. Recognition of it by management builds both the business and the leaders it needs. That's true in the factory, on the sales force, anywhere in the company.

"Naturally there are variations in the talents of individuals and in their desire for responsibility and advancement. But the business will succeed best—and its workers will progress best—*when there is a type of organization* that encourages these qualities as much as possible.

"That's why the leaders of our business decided long ago to find new ways to build people—not just to build things. They worked out a form of organization they thought would accomplish that better.

"Now, most modern businesses *want* to encourage individual development along the lines I'm implying. Many of them have the same objectives we have. But the important question is whether the management is able to move energetically toward those ends. We think that in the line system they're stymied. We think that with our method we're free to go ahead."

THE UNIT SYSTEM

Instead of line organization the National Lamp Works chose what may be called the "unit system," for want of a better name. The company structure was divided into units of such a size that the manager in charge of each one could be personally acquainted with each worker and well informed about his or her abilities, current and potential.

The manager had full responsibility for his unit in every practical respect. If it produced favorable results according to well-defined measuring sticks, he received the credit. If it failed to produce satisfactory results he was also held primarily responsible.

At the same time, the manager had full *authority* in all matters concerning his unit, except for such minimum authority as was specifically reserved for the general manager of the National Lamp Works. *That was the key factor* in making National's organization different from the usual business operation.

"That's just the opposite," the factory manager said, "of what you have in most companies. Usually it works this way: The top boss keeps all the authority except what he turns over specifically to the next guy in line. Then that fellow—the sales manager, perhaps—keeps all the power he can lay hands on except what he's willing to give specifically to his district sales managers. And so on down the line.

"The district manager is told when he takes his job, 'You can do these five things. Everything else must be passed on up the chain of command for approval.'

"In our business we try to eliminate titles and straw bosses between the general manager and the unit manager. Every unit manager is responsible directly to the general manager, and to him only, for the success of his unit's operation.

"The general manager reserves authority on matters affecting the business as a whole. If we're going to bring out a new product, he has final jurisdiction—not the factory manager who might produce that product in his plant. But if that factory manager needs to hire ten more girls as machine operators in order to reach the required production level, that's his business. No one—not even the general manager—can forbid him to do so. All he has to do is to turn out the product at a certain high quality standard and a certain low unit cost, both of which meet the yardsticks measuring his performance. And believe me, those yardsticks are exact and they've been worked out with his participation.

"Suppose we're temporarily short of a certain type of lamp because of material shortages at the factories. Then a district sales manager can sell only his fair percentage of the total current supply. The right of decision there is kept by the general manager. But the great majority of decisions can and must be made by the unit manager.

"We call it the 'Authority Reserved' system. Each unit manager gets what is in effect an Authority Reserved charter, restricted to a few basic points. That tells him what *is* under headquarters control. Beyond that he's on his own, and he has plenty of room to move."

In modern business it is impossible to provide in advance for many of the problems that arise. The National Lamp Works management found that action to solve such problems without wasteful delays was much more likely under the Authority Reserved system than under a line operation. The unit manager could act on most questions without having to pass them on to a higher echelon. Just at the time when delay and buck-passing were most likely, this method could operate normally and smoothly.

The difference also showed up in the spirit of the organization. Individuals enjoyed greater freedom of action. While Authority Reserved did not extend formally beyond the unit manager, in practice there was a strong tendency to pass it along to subordinates. A manager experienced the benefits of the system in his own work. Consequently he was likely to define to his section heads, foremen, etc., the authority he reserved to himself; then he allowed them to deal with all other matters that affected their operations. Ideally this extended to clerks, stenographers, machine operators, and all other employees.

From the beginning the Nela Park departments were operated as *services*. It was not the function of a G-E Lamp headquarters office to direct the factories, sales districts, and other units throughout the country. Instead, it aided them in achieving their objectives.

In the management's viewpoint and planning, the most essential and important units in the business were the factories and the sales districts—not Nela Park. The district employees and the factory employees could feel that the Nela Park people were backing them rather than trying to goad or drive.

Terry, Tremaine, and T. W. Frech, as pioneers of the National business, constantly worked to sustain and implement this new type of business management. They found that it was successful, not only in profitable operation but in the unity, drive, and comradely spirit it produced.

CHAPTER 11

Distribution Plan and License Agreements

As the National Lamp Works and the Edison Lamp Works assessed their situation in early 1912, they found licensing and distribution problems that needed attention. The court decree of 1911 required changes in the marketing system for lamps and highlighted the questions of patents and licenses. These were separate questions. A new distribution system was not linked with patent licensing, but both had to be reviewed at this time.

A NEW DISTRIBUTION SYSTEM

The 1911 decree had forbidden the fixing of resale prices. Prior to 1911, lamp manufacturers had three general classes of customers: (1) large consumers; (2) wholesalers and retailers, who resold the lamps to consumers; and (3) electric-utility companies, which resold to consumers or used the so-called "free renewal" plan. It was important to the manufacturers to see that the ultimate consumer received the right lamp for each purpose. The question now was how to maintain the best possible manufacturer-consumer relations in the use of the product.

General Electric decided to work out an entirely new plan of distribution. Adam Page, Edison sales manager, was largely responsible for conceiving the agency-distribution plan.

One type of sale was not affected by the new system: direct purchase contracts between General Electric and a large consumer. For example, a salesman from a General Electric district office might conclude a purchase agreement with the owner of a large factory. All the lamps used by the factory over a year's time would be subject to that contract. No agent would be involved.

Many sales, however, passed through other channels of distribution. For instance, a company called the Sterling Electric Supply Co. of Stamford, Conn., dealing in electrical goods at the wholesale level, might want to serve as an agent for lamp bulbs made by G.E. Sterling would deal with two kinds of customers: large consumers, such as a local factory; and dealers in electrical goods, such as the Acme Electric Store in the nearby town of Riverside.

Under the agency plan started in 1912, Sterling would be designated as a "B" agent for General Electric lamps. Sterling would represent G.E. in getting a lamp contract from the factory. Sterling would also represent G.E. in arranging the appointment of Acme Electric as a retail agent for General Electric lamps. In neither case would Sterling own the lamps, but would receive them on consignment and then supply the necessary service to customers —stocking, delivery as needed, credit, etc.

The Acme Electric Store would act as an "A" agent for General Electric. Shoppers coming into the store could buy bulbs as needed for their homes. In these transactions Acme would supply the lamps from a consigned stock owned by G.E.

This, in essence, was the agency plan. There were various subclasses of agents and many ramifications of procedure, but the two main types of agency were "B" and "A." The lamps all belonged to General Electric until sold to a user by an agent or placed in use by the agent for his own needs. The agent simply represented G.E. and provided the local services required to serve the consumer.

An agent received compensation from General Electric for the many services he performed for G.E.—display of the lamps in his place of business, delivery to consumers, etc. The compensation paid made it good business for agents at both the wholesale and the retail level.

Agency contracts grew to be somewhat complicated because of the many types of wholesalers and retailers. General Electric worked out a set of sales rules to be followed by Edison and National salesmen. Then, to referee the application of these sales rules, a supervisor's office was established. The supervisor examined contracts to see that they conformed with the correct legal and commercial practice. He ruled on hundreds of questions that arose in the heat of competitive selling, such as whether a particular firm was entitled to a "B" agency or an "A" agency, and so on.

Under its license, Westinghouse was required to sell on terms and at prices that were not more favorable than General Electric's. However, this applied only to lamps made under G-E patents. And Westinghouse was not required to use an agency plan. Nevertheless, the advantages of the agency system were apparent and Westinghouse adopted the same type of distribution system.

The license provided that if Westinghouse used the agency plan, it would not offer better terms to its agents than G.E. offered to General Electric agents. The supervisor's office received the Westinghouse agency contracts for review and the supervisor acted on them just as he did with General Electric agency appointments.

The Department of Justice was fully informed of the details of the agency system. Attorney General George W. Wickersham stated that he was fully satisfied that it was adopted in good faith.

The agency system brought advantages to the public, to the agents, and to the manufacturers who employed it.

Consumers enjoyed the assurance of getting top-quality lamps at established prices. They could be certain, too, that full-scale research would continue to improve quality further and bring about better and better lighting.

In effect the public was also insured against cheapening of the product, which would add considerably to the cost of light. Lamps themselves account for only a small part of that cost. A slight decrease in lamp efficiency, however, can materially increase the unit cost of light because of poor utilization of electric current. So the consumer's stake in lamp quality is high.

Agents handling the lamps were assured of compensation at a steady, reasonable rate. They had no investment to make—no tie-up of capital in lamp stocks. Maintained quality of product meant greater public acceptance and more agency compensation earned. There was no risk by the agent of being left with obsolete stock on hand. The small agent sold at the same price as the large agent.

To General Electric the agency plan represented similar advantages. It meant a stable price structure throughout the marketing chain; the maintenance of continued research for product improvement; and a strong distribution system because of satisfied agents at all levels of distribution.

THE WESTINGHOUSE "A" LICENSE

The patent for Dr. Whitney's Gem lamp had been issued in 1909. The Just and Hanaman patent, covering tungsten lamps, was granted in February, 1912. Dr. Coolidge's final patent application on the ductile-tungsten lamp was almost ready (applied for in July, 1912, and patent issued in December, 1913).

Westinghouse wanted to continue making lamps under the General Electric patents. So on March 1, 1912, G.E. granted Westinghouse a new license covering the patented lamps. This agreement was called the "A" license. It specified the percentage that Westinghouse could produce of the total number of patented lamps made by the two companies. Manufacturer's prices and terms of sale on the patented lamps made by Westinghouse could not be more favorable than General Electric's. A royalty rate was established, which Westinghouse paid to G.E. on the Westinghouse lamps made under General Electric patents.

A new feature of this license was the permission Westinghouse received to use the MAZDA trademark on lamps conforming to MAZDA service standards. This meant that Westinghouse would receive the benefits of General Electric lamp research as these were introduced though the MAZDA system. Since this was a cross licensing agreement, G.E. would also have the right to utilize improvements in products and manufacturing methods devised by Westinghouse in the lamp field.

As stated before (Chapter 7), MAZDA was the mark of a service, not the name of a product. Westinghouse identified itself as the manufacturer of its MAZDA lamps by calling them "Westing-house MAZDA lamps." In the same way, General Electric's two major lamp divisions identified their MAZDA products as "Edison MAZDA" and "National MAZDA." (Not until about 25 years later was the name "G-E MAZDA" utilized for the entire output of MAZDA lamps made by General Electric.)

Not all lamps made by these companies were entitled to the MAZDA trademark—far from it. A type of lamp that was, so to speak, a candidate for MAZDA honors had to be submitted to the careful scrutiny of Hawkins and Fisher at the General Electric Research Laboratory in Schenectady. Along with it went the details about its fabrication. Not until the MAZDA service authorities agreed that the lamp was produced with the benefits of "the latest and best research and manufacturing techniques" did it receive the MAZDA mark.

THE "B" LICENSES

At this time many relatively small manufacturers were making tungsten lamps without patent rights. Obviously the validity of General Electric's tungsten-lamp patents had to be established Therefore G.E. brought suit against one of the infringers, the Laco-Philips company, in the Federal courts. (Laco-Philips did not make lamps in the United States but sold a sizable volume of imported tungsten bulbs.)

This action resulted in a decision upholding the Just and Hana-man patent in the District Court of Southern New York in February, 1916. An appeals court agreed with this decision a few months later.

General Electric now faced a difficult problem. G.E. could put several manufacturers out of business because they were making and selling tungsten lamps that infringed the General Electric patents. If the management had desired to entrench the company firmly in a monopoly position, here was a remarkable opportunity to do so. Proceeding against the infringers would be perfectly justified under the law.

But the company did not want to take this step against firms that had made substantial investments and employed fairly large staffs of workers. Instead, G.E. offered licenses to companies that had been in business prior to the court decision against Laco-Philips.

These companies were called "B" licensees. Each licensee could manufacture lamps under G-E patents, the amount to be a certain percentage of the total number of patented lamps made by General Electric and the licensee combined. The licensees were free to set their own prices and terms of sale. Most of the companies concerned made either large lamps only or miniature lamps only, and they were so licensed. Two of them received licenses for both large and miniature lamps. The licenses specified a royalty rate to be paid to G.E. on patented lamps made by the licensees. Since the sales quotas were figured on an annual basis, the business of a licensee could grow each year in proportion to the growth of General Electric lamp sales. The "B" licensees did not receive the right to use the MAZDA trade-mark.

Altogether, eight companies received "B" licenses in 1916, and 24 more during the next nine years. Many of these companies were consolidated with others as time went on. In almost all cases, when one company bought another, G.E. allowed the purchasing company to take over the license of the company purchased.

Through the licenses General Electric brought to almost the entire industry the remarkable advances in lampmaking that had been achieved from 1904 to 1916. Most of these had resulted from General Electric research. The others had been acquired by G.E. in its continual efforts to make G-E lamps better through any and all scientific advances.

CHAPTER 12

Pure Science and Applied Science

GENERAL ELECTRIC carried on two types of research and development in the lamp business. One was fundamental scientific inquiry conducted without regard to product. The other comprised the direct improvement of products, parts, machinery, and manufacturing techniques—in other words, applied research having commercial objectives. The first of these activities was of course typified by the General Electric Research Laboratory.

One of the leading figures in the history of the laboratory appeared on the scene July 19, 1909. That was the day when Irving Langmuir, a 29-year-old chemist, first went to work at Schenectady. He had won a degree in metallurgical engineering at Columbia University in 1903. He had studied chemistry under Nernst for three years at the University of Göttingen in Germany, where he received his Ph.D., and then had taught at Stevens Institute of Technology before joining Whitney, Coolidge, and the other General Electric scientists.

Dr. Whitney turned Langmuir loose to select any problem in the laboratory that he wished to study. As Langmuir looked around, he noticed the blackening of lamp bulbs on the test racks; as they darkened, the lamps emitted less and less light. He decided to explore the problem of blackening. The getters used up to that time (see Chapter 7) reduced bulb blackening somewhat but it remained a most troublesome phenomenon. The high vacuum did not eliminate all the gases in the atmosphere; water vapor also remained in the bulbs in minute quantities.

One of the most critical commentators on the lamp business has said of Langmuir's self-selected assignment: "No specific commercial results were expected; Langmuir merely hoped to learn more about the behavior of gases in incandescent lamps."

His studies continued for three years before he answered the questions he had asked himself.

First he asked, "What gases are present in the vacuum bulbs?" He found minute quantities of several different gases or vapors: oxygen, carbon dioxide, carbon monoxide, hydrogen, hydrocarbon vapor, nitrogen, and water vapor. Langmuir had to work out new methods and use new vacuum apparatus to analyze the presence of all these gases in *1 cubic millimeter* of total volume at atmospheric pressure.

Second, he found that most of the gases had little or no discoloring effect. However, the presence of water vapor and the gradual evaporation of tungsten atoms from the filament resulted in a complicated cycle of blackening. In this little atomic dance even a microscopic amount of water vapor could cause a rather large amount of tungsten to be carried to the glass wall of the bulb. The vapor was renewed at the conclusion of each cycle and was ready to act again as a partner to the tungsten atoms in the darkening of the bulb.

But which was the real offender—the action of the water vapor or the evaporation of the filament? To find out, Langmuir made tests in which lamps were kept completely immersed in liquid air. This prevented water vapor from coming into contact with the filament. The rate of blackening was exactly the same as before.

These experiments led to two conclusions: The bulb blackening was due to evaporation of the filament; and consequently, the blackening could not be eliminated by improving the vacuum even if it were possible to produce an absolutely perfect vacuum.

FREEDOM OF RESEARCH

Langmuir had worked steadily for two years to get this far— and there were still many questions to be answered. His explanation of the work up to that time reveals not only his interesting "pure science" approach but the attitude of Dr. Whitney and the G-E management as well:

"I really didn't know how to produce a better vacuum, and instead proposed to study the bad effects of gases by putting gases in the lamp. I hoped that in this way I could extrapolate to zero gas pressure and thus predict, without really trying it, how good the lamp would be if we could produce a perfect vacuum.

"This principle of research I have found extremely useful on many occasions. When it is suspected that some useful result is to be obtained by avoiding certain undesired factors, but it is found that these factors are very difficult to avoid, then it is a good plan to increase deliberately each of these factors in turn so as to exaggerate their bad effects, and thus become so familiar with them that one can determine whether it is really worth while to avoid them. For example, if you have in lamps a vacuum as good as you know how to produce, but suspect that the lamps would be better if you had a vacuum, say, one hundred times as good, it may be the best policy, instead of attempting to devise methods of improving this vacuum, to spoil the vacuum deliberately in known ways and you may find then that no improvement in vacuum is needed or just how much better the vacuum needs to be.

"During these first few years, while I was thus having such a good time satisfying my curiosity and publishing scientific papers on chemical reactions at low pressures, I frequently wondered whether it was fair that I should spend my whole time in an industrial organization on such purely scientific work, for I confess I didn't see what applications could be made of it, nor did I even have any applications in mind. Several times I talked the matter over with Dr. Whitney, saying that I could not tell where this work was going to lead us. He replied that it was not necessary, as far as he was concerned, that it should lead anywhere. He would like to see me continue working along any fundamental lines that would give us more information in regard to the phenomena taking place in incandescent lamps, and said that I should feel myself perfectly free to go ahead on any such lines that seemed of interest to me. For nearly three years I worked in this way with several assistants before any real application was made of any of my work. In adopting this broad-minded attitude Dr. Whitney showed himself to be a real pioneer in the new type of modern industrial research." .

GAS-FILLED LAMPS

The third major step in Langmuir's research was to study the rate of evaporation from tungsten filaments at different temperatures, both in vacuum and in inert gases at various pressures.

He found that the presence of an inert gas such as nitrogen reduced evaporation considerably. The nitrogen had the effect of obstructing the path of the tungsten atoms on their way to the wall of the glass bulb. At the same time it helped to prevent the water vapor from picking up tungsten atoms and escorting them to the glass surface.

This was fine, but scientists find that there are drawbacks to many of their findings that appear favorable. So it was with the effects of introducing an inert gas into the bulbs. The nitrogen increased the loss of heat from the filament, and this reduced the efficiency (light output) of the lamp. The decrease in efficiency was greater than the gain realized from a smaller amount of blackening. In effect Langmuir had taken one good stride forward, only to be pushed two steps backward. He still had to search for some additional factor that would create an over-all improvement.

Some of the lamps made by Sawyer and Man, Farmer, and other early experimenters had used gas fillings. Edison had tried to develop a gas-filled lamp. But all these attempts, in the carbon-lamp era, had been unsuccessful. No one really understood the effects of gases in lamps until Langmuir's explorations found the facts.

As a final procedure he studied the loss of heat from small wires in gas. And here he made a key discovery: The heat loss caused by the gases did not increase proportionately as the size of the filament was increased. Of course there was an upper limit to this, but a larger filament could be used than had been thought feasible. The favorable effects of the gas filling would more than counterbalance the heat losses, and the larger filament would permit operation at higher temperature and therefore higher brightness. A gas-filled lamp could operate at about 2500°C, some 400° above the filament temperature in a vacuum lamp.

Scarcely less significant was Langmuir's finding that, if the filament was closely coiled, the diameter of the spiral coil was the determining factor in the loss of heat, rather than the diameter of the filament wire itself.

Thus the increased efficiency of the new lamps he created, together with the reduction in blackening, represented striking gains in illumination. Langmuir had set out simply to get as much information as possible about the effects of the various gases in existing lamp bulbs. He finished by developing a new type of lamp—the first truly successful gas-filled incandescent lamp—with vastly increased efficiency throughout its life.

The first gas-filled tungsten lamps were introduced commercially by G.E. (Edison and National) in 1913. They were called MAZDA C lamps to distinguish them from the vacuum (MAZDA B) lamps. The first sizes placed on the market were 750-watt and 1,000-watt bulbs. The increase in efficiency was greatest in these sizes. Also it was in these large bulbs that the necessary knowledge to make the application was first obtained.

Later the laboratory and the factories learned how to apply the idea to other sizes: 200-watt through 500-watt gas-filled lamps were introduced in 1914; the 100-watt bulb in 1917; and smaller sizes in later years, down to and including the standard 40-watt bulb.

Total efficiency over the rated life of the lamps was *doubled* in the 750-watt and 1,000-watt sizes. In smaller sizes the gain was less but added greatly to lamp quality and cut the cost of light. The increase was 25 per cent in the 100-watt lamp, for example. The initial efficiency of the 100-watt gas-filled bulb was 12.5 lumens per watt; in the 60-watt lamp, 11.1 lpw.

Dr. Langmuir applied for a patent on these lamps in April, 1913, and it was granted three years later. He went on to dozens of other scientific achievements. The list of medals and other awards he has earned from learned societies is long and lustrous, topped by the Nobel prize in chemistry for 1932. He thus joined the select group of which his former teacher, Walther Nernst, was a member. Nernst had won the same Nobel award in 1920.

From 1909 through 1915 the laboratory expended nearly $200,000 on Langmuir's work and the development of gas-filled lamps. Yet this investment—and the business structure that provided the research money—proved amply justified. The years of effort by Langmuir and his assistants added millions of dollars in lighting value for consumers of lamps—and the value total is still growing day by day and year by year.

Gas-filled lamps found a ready market because of their much higher efficiency. They delivered a crushing blow to carbon-arc lighting except for a few specialized applications. Gas-filled lamps were much superior on all counts for street lighting, which had been a last outpost for extensive use of arc lighting.

At first nitrogen was used in the new lamps, though Langmuir recognized and specified the value of argon gas for the purpose. After argon became commercially available in quantity (from 1919 on) most of the gas content in standard lamps was argon, mixed with a small quantity of nitrogen.

NONSAG WIRE

Meanwhile lamp development—applied science as contrasted with pure science—kept pace with the needs for better illumination.

Just as blackening had been a thorny problem, so were the "offsetting" of tungsten crystals in the filament and the sagging of the coils in the coiled wire. Both of these difficulties quite often caused lamps to burn out before the end of rated life. As always, the laboratory and factory men were dissatisfied with the best product they knew how to make. So they kept on trying to learn how to make the lamps still better.

The man who overcame these deficiencies demonstrated the infinite patience of the true scientist. He was Dr. Aladar Pacz of the Lamp Development Laboratory at Nela Park. He performed experiment after experiment—*218 in all*—and finally arrived at a process that produced nonsag filament wire. The coils in this new type of wire remained properly separated, tiny fractions of an inch apart. Offsetting within the wire was greatly reduced, and there was much less breakage of filaments. Dr. Pacz made his patent application in February, 1917, and the Patent Office approved it in March, 1922.

MAZDA service and a detailed standardizing procedure carried the needed information to the factories, so that such discoveries as gas-filled lamps and nonsag wire could be applied in mass production. Lampmaking could be standardized in the various factories by precise and thorough outlining of procedures, and this has been the important function of a department in the Lamp Division for many years. The results are uniformity and dependability of product, good cost control, and efficient training of factory employees. Standardizing helps maintain skill and knowledge throughout the manufacturing organization.

BUILDING BETTER MACHINES

Machine work moved forward rapidly during the years 1912 to 1917. More than ever the work of lampmaking became the function of dependable automatic processing, leaving human hands and brains free to supervise and improve. To make lead-in wires, G-E experts developed a double electric-welding machine. They built an improved sealing-in machine, an automatic machine for inserting the wires supporting the filament, and an automatic exhaust machine. Cement for lamp bases was inserted automatically. The Equipment Works built more and more duplicates of these mechanical marvels as lamp demand soared and new factories came into existence. They built variations on each type as well, so that the making of miniature bulbs and specialized lamps would proceed as efficiently as the manufacture of standard large lamps.

National, of course, had operated the Fostoria Glass Works prior to 1911. General Electric took over this property, along with the other National plants. (The same was true of the Providence Base Works at Providence, R.I., which at that time was the only plant manufacturing a full line of lamp bases.)

To further the research work in glass, the Glass Technology Laboratory was established at Cleveland in 1916 and the Glass Machine Works in 1919.

In 1912 the Empire Machine Co., a subsidiary of Corning, developed a semiautomatic bulb-blowing machine. Here was the first in a long series of machines that were to pare costs and speed the production of bulbs phenomenally. General Electric obtained a license to make and use the Empire machine, and G-E technicians developed it further. Bulb output leaped to about 350 per hour per machine employing one skilled and two unskilled operators.

At the Westlake Machine Co., which was a property of the Libbey Glass Co., machine designers toiled for several years to construct an even better bulb-blowing machine. The Westlake machine, completely automatic, was used on an experimental basis in 1917 and 1918. Then, as it was gradually perfected, it took over a much larger share of bulb output, along with an improved, fully automatic Empire machine called the Empire "F." G.E. also negotiated for a license on the Westlake development (in 1918). The men in the Glass Machine Works and the glass factories contributed many of the advancements that led to fully automatic operation. Carl A. Brown was a notable leader in this work.

A new type of lime glass had to be formulated for use with these machines, in contrast to the lead glass formerly used for hand blowing. (The shortage of potash during World War I also made the change necessary.) The researchers in the Glass Technology Laboratory worked this out after much careful experimentation, along with similar investigation by Corning.

Edward Danner of the Libbey Glass Co. obtained a patent in 1917 on an automatic machine for drawing glass tubing and cane. General Electric purchased the rights to this development so far as it pertained to lamp glass; this was part of the license agreement concluded with Libbey for the Westlake machine.

As the company's technicians in the glass field improved all these machines, the output of bulbs and tubing mounted and costs dropped sharply. This was another prime example of applied science.

From theoretical investigations to product development and factory improvements, General Electric was fulfilling the industry's needs in both the Edison and the National Lamp Works. The company's responsibilities to the public in the lamp business were being met here as well as in the fields of business management and marketing.

CHAPTER 13

Helping to Win Wartime Victories

WHEN THE UNITED STATES entered World War I the nation was not well prepared. We lacked trained fighting men and badly needed munitions. Equally serious was the fact that there were no adequate plans and methods for utilizing American research, development, and manufacturing skills.

However, America's producers responded to the emergency in every way possible. Those in the lamp industry were typical in this respect.

Men volunteered for the armed forces from the Edison and National plants and offices all across the country. Like their fellow Americans, many of them served with distinction in all branches of the services—and again like their compatriots, some gave their lives or were wounded in battle.

The contributions of industry and of those ineligible for military service of course cannot be compared to the sacrifices made by the men in uniform. Nevertheless, the lamp companies were among the first industrial organizations to offer their resources, scientific skill, and manpower to the government for whatever needs they could fill. Both the Edison and the National Lamp Works did this during the first few days after the declaration of war (April 6, 1917).

CHEMICAL WARFARE WORK

One of the fields in which the Army asked for help was chemical warfare. The German army had used poison gas as early as

April, 1915. The Allied armies were not equipped to combat gas warfare. At first they used hastily prepared, makeshift respirators. Later they retaliated with their own gas attacks. When the United States entered the war there was need for efficient gas masks and for developments in all types of chemical warfare, from basic research all the way through the manufacturing stage.

The National Lamp Works was enlisted by the government in this work in April, 1917. National was associated with the National Carbon Co. in this effort, especially in the development work on gas masks. Several other chemical manufacturers participated in the production of offensive weapons. In the beginning this was under the direction of the Bureau of Mines.

In charge of this activity for National was Frank M. Dorsey, a chemical engineer prominent in the work of the Lamp Development Laboratory. His chief assistant was Dale C. Hughes, and several others from the laboratory formed the central group around which the project grew. Dorsey served first as a civilian. Later he was sworn into the Chemical Warfare Service of the Army, along with a number of other Nela Park men. He received his commission as a colonel when this new branch of the Army was first organized in 1918. He continued his work at Nela Park as chief of the Development Division of the Chemical Warfare Service. Other officers and men, some from National and some from outside the company, were assigned to the group until the total quartered at Nela Park reached about 250.

Several Nela Park personalities prominent in later years aided in the chemical warfare program. Dale Hughes managed a variety of assignments and completed his war service as a captain. Following the war he became secretary of the manufacturing committee at Nela Park and served in that capacity for more than 30 years. Leo G. Cover of the Cleveland Wire Works was another of Dorsey's assistants, holding the rank of captain in the Chemical Warfare Service. After the war he returned to the Wire Works and advanced to the position of manager before his retirement in 1952. Marvin Pipkin, who later was responsible for the development of inside frosting of lamps, was a young chemist serving as a private in the chemical warfare unit. His research work in the various projects was outstanding and after the war he joined the Lamp Development Laboratory staff. There were many others who willingly took on their assignments to this strange and difficult operation and then returned to the more prosaic but constructive job of making lamps.

RADIO AND X-RAY TUBES

Both radio and the use of X rays may be said to have come into real prominence and usefulness during World War I. Here the men and women in lamp manufacturing found somewhat more familiar ground. The armed services greatly needed radio and X-ray tubes—and these resembled highly complicated and expensive lamps.

Not long before the United States declared war, Dr. Langmuir and his associates at Schenectady had developed much improved radio tubes. However, there was still only laboratory production. For that matter, no large-scale manufacturing of tubes existed anywhere in the country. Radio was still an infant industry in every sense. In August, 1917, the Schenectady laboratory asked both the Edison and the National Lamp Works to help in carrying the work from the laboratory to volume production.

W. R. Burrows at Harrison and W. H. Roberts at Nela Park assumed the task and their staffs plunged into this activity at once. As an important part of its contribution, the Edison Lamp Works cooperated with the Schenectady laboratory and the Providence Base Works in producing satisfactory bases for the tubes.

Philip J. Pritchard of the Nela Lamp Division headed the tube-manufacturing operations at Cleveland. He and his associates faced an enormously difficult production job. New methods and machines—adapted from lampmaking practice—had to be contrived for every step of manufacture.

Scores of difficulties and seemingly conclusive failures marked the early weeks. Yet by the end of 1917 volume production of vacuum tubes was under way. On Jan. 4, 1918, the Vacuum Tube Division of General Electric was formally organized with Pritch-

NEW
and
BETTER
and
COSTS LESS

This advertisement was one of the first offering a great new advance in lampmaking—the inside-frosted bulb (*Saturday Evening Post*, May 15, 1926).

NATIONAL MAZDA

A GENERAL ELECTRIC PRODUCT

See it at any store
which handles
National MAZDA Lamps

IT LOOKS different from the lamp you have been used to. It *is* different—*improved in every way.* Pearl-gray in color, its frosting on the *inside* of the bulb, it's the last word in lamps for home-lighting.

Notice These Advantages!

Better light—and also more light—for the same current, which means both eye-saving and money-saving.

Easy to clean, because the outside of the bulb is smooth glass (the frosting's on the *inside*). Dust can't stick to it, and cut down its light.

Better looking, for its pearl-gray bulb takes on the tint of colors which surround it.

More rugged, stronger than previous types.

Costs less—in both first cost and maintenance.

NATIONAL LAMP WORKS
of General Electric Company
NELA PARK, CLEVELAND, OHIO

The New
NATIONAL MAZDA
Lamp

Marvin Pipkin, of the Lamp Development Laboratory, whose ingenuity developed the inside-frost process in 1924 and more than 20 years later also devised the Q-coat for G-E white bulbs. He is shown holding a sample of each of these bulb types.

In the inspection process shown here, lamp filaments are magnified about 60 times on a projection screen, making the checkup easier and more accurate.

Here is an example of basic research in the Science of Seeing. S. K. Guth (standing) and A. A. Eastman (seated) are pictured as they developed some of the fundamental data on eye movements while reading under varying amounts of light.

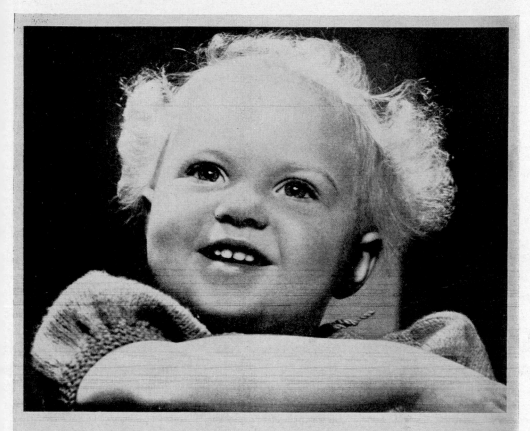

ONE OF THE TEN MILLION CHILDREN WHO NEED *LIGHT CONDITIONING*

OF ten million school children today, about two million have defective eyesight. One reason for this tragic condition is the habit of using eyes for close seeing in poor light. Only recently has research disclosed the important part that proper lighting can play in help-

ing eyes see more easily, without strain. Today this new kind of eyesight protection is called "Light Conditioning," the science of Better Light for Better Sight. Light conditioning is simply providing the right amount of light and the right kind of lighting for eyes at work or play. For example, you can start to light condition your living room ... today ... for as little as fifteen or twenty cents. One new Edison MAZDA lamp of the proper size often makes a surprising difference in the amount of light you get for your seeing task. Your electric lighting company has a free

light conditioning service. Just phone, and a trained Lighting Advisor will measure your lighting with a Light Meter and show you how to light condition your home.

SEND FOR FREE BOOKLET

Meanwhile, you can get a free booklet that tells all about the fascinating subject of Light Conditioning. Gives dozens of easy, inexpensive ways to make seeing easier and safer for your family. For free copy, send a post card to General Electric Company, Dept. 166, Nela Park, Cleveland, O.

now only
15¢
For 15-25-40 and 60 watts
They stay brighter longer

THE FIRST STEP TO LIGHT CONDITIONING ... CHANGE TO THE NEW AND BRIGHTER

EDISON MAZDA LAMPS
GENERAL ⊗ ELECTRIC

One of the early advertisements on better light for better sight, illustrating General Electric's interest in selling better seeing as well as better lamps (*Saturday Evening Post*, Aug. 28, 1937).

SAFER NIGHT

Brought about through the united efforts of the automobile manufacturers, the makers of headlighting equipment and safety and state authorities.

See farther! See quicker! See better!

After three years of continuous development in the laboratory and on the road, comes one of the greatest contributions to safety on the highways at night... the Sealed Beam headlighting system.

● Prepare for a new motoring thrill when you get behind the wheel of a 1940 car at night! You'll be amazed at how much better you can see with the new Sealed Beam Headlighting System... how much safer you feel... and how much more ease and comfort you enjoy.

WHY THIS NEW HEADLIGHTING IS BETTER

Sealed Beam headlighting uses a new type of headlight that combines in one *sealed unit,* lens, reflector and light source.

It provides more light. It puts more light *where you need it* for safer, quicker, easier seeing. *There is no appreciable loss in light during the life of the unit!* You get new car lighting throughout the life of the car.

The Traffic Beam puts more light ahead on the right side, and more light on both sides of the road close to the car. When properly aimed, it is glare-free. Test car drivers tell us that it makes the road wider because it cuts down that tendency to hug the center line.

The Country Beam puts more light ahead and more light on the road shoulders at both sides to help you see farther and see hazards quicker. An indicator light on the dash reminds you when it is "on," and a simple foot switching arrangement, standard on 1940 cars, makes it simple to shift to the traffic beam when meeting other cars.

WHAT THE NEW SEALED BEAM SYSTEM MEANS TO THE BUYER OF A 1940 CAR

Greater Safety for you and for others. This new system gives you more light for safer seeing in city or country.

Greater Comfort through less eyestrain and fatigue... less annoyance from glare... easier, surer seeing. With this new Sealed Beam headlighting, you will want to drive more at night and you will feel safer when you do it. Try driving a 1940 car at night and see for yourself.

To get the most out of your Present Car Lighting

The Sealed Beam Headlighting system is available only on new cars. To get the greatest safety and comfort from old style headlamps, be sure to do these things:

1. Have reflectors cleaned and polished twice a year.
2. Replace blackened and burned out bulbs.
3. Have headlamps aimed twice a year.
4. Always use traffic (lower) beam when meeting other cars.

GENERAL ⊕ ELECTRIC

FOR SAFER SEEING... ALWAYS USE YOUR TRAFFIC BEAM WHEN MEETING OTHER CARS

Look at these Safety and Comfort advantages ➡

SEE FARTHER. This new kind of headlighting puts more light DOWN the road to let you see farther than ever before at night. That means a bigger margin of safety; and new comfort, too.

SEE QUICKER. Because this new Sealed Beam system gives you more light, you pick out unexpected hazards faster, have more time to act. That means protection for you and for others.

SEE BETTER. The new Sealed Beam headlight put more light ON the road. And they throw more light of each side, on shoulders and ditches, so you see better and more clearly.

This two-page advertisement told the public about the advantages of General Electric's

BY 1940 CARS*

DRIVING!

...with the new
SEALED BEAM
HEADLIGHTING
SYSTEM

*Standard equipment on most 1940 models

When NEW	SEALED BEAM HEADLIGHTING Practically no loss of light	2 Years Old

SEE WHAT A DIFFERENCE!

When NEW	PRIOR TYPE HEADLIGHTING As much as 50% loss in light	2 Years Old

New sealed beam headlight, combines light source, reflector and lens in one sealed unit... Better, safer, more efficient.

Here is the same stretch of road, the same hazards, at night. But just look at the difference in what you see with these four headlighting conditions. 1. Sealed Beam Headlighting (new). Note the pedestrian and curve ahead. 2. And after two years' service. Practically no change in seeing. 3. Old-style headlighting (new). Pedestrian barely visible. 4. After two years' use without headlight service.

air and moisture leakage   NEW   PRIOR TYPE   permanently sealed

GLARE-FREE TRAFFIC BEAM. Light from this new system is so accurately controlled, that the traffic beam, when properly aimed, is glare-free. Always use it in the city and when meeting other cars.

CURVES ARE CLEARER . . . entire width of road usable. With more light on road shoulders, you see curves quicker, more clearly. The road seems wider. You drive with new ease and confidence.

PERMANENTLY SEALED . . . practically no loss in light. Lens, reflector, and light source form one sealed unit... keeping out fumes, dust, dirt, and oil that dull "old-style" reflectors.

NEW CAR SEEING throughout the life of the car. Because Sealed Beam units not only stay brighter longer but are completely renewed when you have "burn-outs" replaced.

led-beam headlights—greater safety, easier seeing (*Saturday Evening Post*, Oct. 14, 1939).

Val J. Roper and George E. Meese, G-E automotive lighting engineers, set up a new headlighting experiment on the Nela Park test car.

The G-E Lighting Institute at night, as seen across the illuminated pool. Every year thousands of people visit this center of lamp and light-ing information. From school children to lighting specialists, they all learn a little more about good illumination at the Institute.

A typical meeting at the Lighting Institute. The display boards in the background show some of the many types of General Electric lamps.

During Edison Science Week at the Institute, students watch Ben F. Rudolph, a veteran glassblower, as he produces a replica of Edison's first practical lamp.

ard in charge, and with William T. Cogger as special engineer for the project.

Manufacturing problems multiplied throughout the war period. New types of receiving and transmitting tubes were designed at frequent intervals. Each type brought new perplexities, but the lamp men learned how to step up tube life and quality. They filled the needs of the Signal Corps, the Navy, and other service arms. The tubes were used on ships and aircraft as well as at ground stations. New advances occurred almost daily in radio-telephone and radiotelegraph communications.

The X-ray-tube program also originated in the research laboratory in Schenectady. Dr. Langmuir had investigated the effects of electrical discharges through a vacuum. His experiments resulted in the discovery of several previously unknown principles. With this knowledge as a basis, Dr. Coolidge built a radically new type of X-ray tube. The new tube was so satisfactory that the U.S. Army and the Red Cross immediately adopted it as the standard for use in their hospitals overseas. It now was possible also to fill the urgent need of the armed forces for portable X-ray equipment, to be mounted on trucks and used wherever required in the forward areas. Thus the Coolidge tube opened entirely new fields for X-ray usage in both military and civilian life.

The tubes were manufactured at Schenectady on a small scale for several months. By April, 1918, more volume had to be attained and the National organization was asked to help. Again W. H. Roberts, P. J. Pritchard, and their factory workers accepted the assignment. On May 7 the X-Ray Tube Division was organized. There were even fewer precedents for the manufacturing operations in this field than in radio. However, the group began production on schedule, made notable improvements in processing, and achieved excellent output figures during the remaining months of the war. Assembly of the many metal parts for the tube had been accomplished only by expert jewelers in the Schenectady laboratory. At Nela Park young women took over this work and became so dexterous at it that they almost doubled the assembly rate of the skilled laboratory employees.

The new X-ray products contributed much to the treatment of troops during the war and in the immediate postwar period. They also provided a great impetus to effective use of X rays throughout the field of medicine after the war.

OTHER WARTIME ACTIVITIES

The outbreak of war demonstrated to the Allied nations how great had been their dependence on German research laboratories and manufacturing plants for many essential products. One of the most important of these was optical glass. The armed services had to obtain lenses of high quality for range finders, field glasses, periscopes, and similar instruments, all of which had been supplied almost entirely from Europe and particularly from Germany.

The Glass Technology Laboratory at Nela Park, under the direction of W. M. Clark, cooperated with Bausch & Lomb and other manufacturers in this country to help develop better optical glass. The Nela Research Laboratory, headed by Dr. Edward P. Hyde, intensively studied all types of field glasses for the National Research Council, which was the wartime agency supervising scientific work for the armed forces.

Lt. Col. Robert A. Millikan made the original N.R.C. request for the study of binocular and monocular glasses. This was of course the noted Dr. Millikan who was to win the Nobel prize in physics in 1923. Even before his inquiry—and two weeks before the declaration of war—Dr. Hyde had offered the complete facilities of the laboratory to Secretary of War Newton D. Baker.

The Nela Research Laboratory also developed new signal lamps and complete light-signaling units for the War Department. Matthew Luckiesh of the laboratory staff studied camouflage problems and made recommendations for aircraft, ships, and ground installations. Flares and rockets were other subjects for experimental work in the laboratory.

The Engineering Department designed and constructed special machinery for the vacuum-tube activity and devised new procedures for testing the tubes. The engineers also developed landing lights and signal lights for airplanes, searchlights, many types of indicator lights for instrument panels, motor-vehicle lights, and gunsight lamps. They solved problems in camouflage, in the illumination of landing fields for night flying, and in protective lighting for industry to prevent sabotage and theft. These, together with many projects in testing and the creation of new light-measuring instruments, kept the staffs well occupied at both Harrison and Nela Park.

The Standardizing Department aided in the designing of the new lamps required in all branches of warfare. The Chemical Laboratory found its opportunities to serve in the chemical warfare projects. In fact, every department was engaged in the war effort to some degree. Production of lamps for civilian use was curtailed, of course, but both Edison and National supplied the normal products essential to maintaining the nation's economy.

While the achievements of the lamp companies were no more praiseworthy than those of many other industries, they did contribute to victory. They also established a pattern that was to prove highly important when the years of uncertain peace led to a second world war.

CHAPTER 14

The Benefits of Never-ending Research

NOT EVEN a world war could stop the public desire for more and better lighting nor halt the phenomenal expansion of the lamp business. In 1919 the industry produced more than 224 million large lamps with a manufacturer's value of $48 million. This was two and a half times as many lamps as American manufacturers had turned out in 1914. Even this total did not include about $3 million worth of Gem, tantalum, and other specialized types of large lamps, nor about $6 million worth of miniature lamps. So the value of all electric lamps made in 1919 ran to more than $57 million.

As an industry leader, General Electric had to contend with a familiar problem, patent infringement by unlicensed manufacturers. G.E. took legal action during the early 1920's to establish the validity of the Langmuir and Coolidge patents and to end some of the infringements.

The Langmuir patent on gas-filled lamps was upheld in a Federal court in October, 1919, and sustained on appeal in June, 1920. The Coolidge patent on ductile tungsten was also held valid in June, 1920. Some years later in another case the courts ruled that the article claims of this patent were invalid but upheld the method claims. In other words, G.E. could not successfully claim that a *product* (such as a radio tube) using ductile tungsten infringed the patent, though the *process* of producing ductile tungsten was protected by the patent. In any case, G.E. was able to proceed against a dozen infringing lamp manufacturers and bring their violations to at least a temporary halt.

MORE ADVANCES IN LAMP DESIGN

From Edison's time on, large lamps (that is, lamp bulbs for general lighting use) had been made with a small, rather sharp tip of glass at the large end of the bulb. This was where the exhaust tube had been connected to the bulb. When the heated glass was sealed off and the exhaust tube removed, the glass tip formed naturally. There was no known way to eliminate or avoid it, except through a very expensive process.

There had been a few tipless lamps, such as the bulb marketed by Herman J. Jaeger in 1903 and for a few years thereafter. General Electric manufactured the Meridian lamp from 1906 to 1911, and this had a tipless construction originally patented by H. D. Burnett and Samuel E. Doane in 1894. Their idea was not commercially usable until it was improved in 1906 through a machine invention made by Mark H. Branin of the Edison Lamp Works. The Meridian lamp was a decorative type designed to compete with the Nernst lamp (see Chapter 7) and was not manufactured in large quantities. The Jaeger and Meridian tipless constructions were too costly to be employed for more than a few specialized lamps. Both used an exhaust tube inserted in the stem of the lamp.

For many years lamp men had wanted to get rid of that sharp tip. It caused breakage; people sometimes injured themselves on it; all in all, it was a nuisance.

The answer was worked out by two men at Nela Park: L. E. Mitchell and A. J. White. They devised an ingenious improvement on the Jaeger and Burnett-Doane methods. The exhaust tube was inserted in the stem while the stem was being made (instead of afterward, as in Jaeger's lamp) and the bulb could be readily exhausted mechanically at the stem end. The tipless lamp was now economical to make. It was safer, less liable to break, better-looking, and gave better distribution of light. In March, 1919, Mitchell and White applied for patents on the method and the machine they had developed. Patent Office approval was granted in July, 1922. The tipless construction quickly became standard for all general-purpose lamps.

A few years later General Electric effected another major lamp improvement: inside frosting. This, along with tipless construction, brought the appearance of the lamps up to what millions of consumers recognize today as a standard lamp bulb.

Prior to 1925 the great majority of bulbs were made of clear glass. One could see the stem, the support wires, and the white-hot filament. There was glare—lots of it! To reduce this annoying, possibly dangerous glare, General Electric research men tried several methods of treating the glass bulb. The frosted or enameled lamps they developed came on the market and did offer certain advantages, but there were disadvantages that equaled or perhaps overbalanced the benefits except for a few specialized uses.

The use of white glass or white enamel coatings cut down glare and distributed light more evenly than clear glass but resulted in sizable reductions in light output—averaging about 15 per cent. Frosting bulbs on the outside (by etching the glass with acid or by sandblasting) also cut efficiency. The loss of light was about 10 per cent. Furthermore, this method left a rough exterior surface that collected dust and dirt; efficiency over the life of the lamp fell even further as a result.

When the laboratory men tried frosting the inside of the bulb by treating it with acid they found that this weakened the glass so much that breakage became a serious problem. The acid cut tiny sharp crevices in the surface of the glass, and the bulbs were too fragile for ordinary handling.

Marvin Pipkin of the Lamp Development Laboratory continued experimenting with inside frosting. He tried something that apparently didn't make sense, but it worked!

If a structure is weakened by a certain treatment, most people would conclude that doing the same thing a second time would merely weaken it further. But Pipkin didn't jump to this conclusion. He had some distrust of the certainty of the obvious. He took some lamps that had been subjected to one inside-frosting treatment with acid—and gave them another one. This was delib-

erate, not frivolous or accidental. Pipkin had carefully analyzed
the effects of the first acid bath. He had reason to believe that
the second treatment might have different effects.

And the results certainly were different. The second acid etching smoothed off the glass, rounded out the crevices, and produced
a strong, evenly frosted surface. Others had suspected this before,
but Pipkin was the first to make a thorough application of the
idea in the lamp industry and prove its beneficial effects. The
patent he applied for in June, 1925, was granted in October,
1928.

Besides the strength of the inside-frosted bulb, its better appearance, the reduction of glare, and the improved distribution

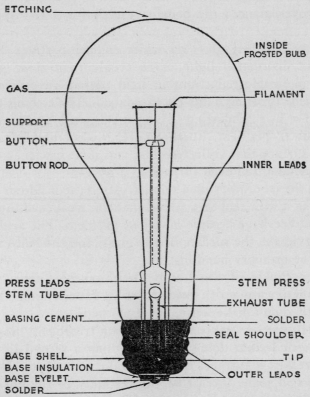

Diagram showing the parts and internal construction of a standard incandescent lamp bulb.

of light, this new product maintained high efficiency. Total light output was only 1 to 1½ per cent less than that of a clear glass lamp. The other advantages far outweighed this slight decrease. Inside frosting was adopted for standard lamps, and a large majority of all lamp bulbs sold from 1925 on had this improvement.

The research men created many other new types of lamps during this period. A complete list would be too lengthy here, but the following are typical:

New types of motion-picture projection lamps (1920 and the following years)

Lamps for airport and cross-country airway lighting (1921 and later years)

Depressible-beam automobile headlight lamps with two filaments for "driving" and "passing" beams (1924)

Lamp design had advanced immeasurably since 1907, not only in the familiar household bulbs but for dozens of other applications, such as specialized commercial and industrial needs, railroad lights, sign lighting, decorative illumination, and new uses for miniature lamps.

PROGRESS IN LAMP ASSEMBLY

W. R. Burrows, the factory-operations expert of the Edison Lamp Works, revolutionized the manufacturing system at Harrison during the years 1918–1921. Until that time every operation in lampmaking was separate and distinct. Each department handled one step in the manufacturing process; there was a department for stem-making, another for filament-mounting, a third for exhaust, etc. Various departments had different rates of production. Partly assembled lamps had to be stored temporarily until the next department was ready to handle them; that took a lot of floor space in the factory. Lamps had to be carried from one department to another, and this increased the chances of breakage or misalignment.

Burrows saw an opportunity to change this system for the

better. "Why not," he thought, "split up the operations differently? Let's have a unit that builds lamps from start to finish, with all the necessary machines combined or located close together in a designated factory space. We can synchronize the machines and the various processes more closely and keep an even flow of lamps going. We'll eliminate much of our temporary storage problem. Then in the next area we'll set up another complete unit and so on—complete units instead of specialized departments."

It sounded easier than it was in practice. Burrows anticipated that and simply kept working at it until, after three years, he had the unit system. The results were excellent in terms of increased output at the Harrison plant. In the early stages of the switch to the unit-production system, productivity per man-hour almost doubled. Over-all output, including the time of all production workers, reached 18 lamps per man-hour as compared to about 10 previously. A unit employing five operators to handle practically all the lamp-assembly processes could turn out about 350 lamps per hour. The savings in floor space were also impressive.

Machine developments multiplied during the years after World War I in both National and Edison plants. They included a machine for inserting filament supports at high speed; a machine to make stems for the tipless construction; one to make hot-cut flares for stems; another to coil filaments—an important step. In 1924 the Sealex machine appeared, to exhaust the bulbs, fill them with gas, and seal them. Various mechanical steps accomplished the inside frosting, the sealing of several sizes of bulbs, improved coiling and filament mounting, and faster, better basing of lamps. Machine speeds were increased from time to time, so that a complete lampmaking unit could work in marvelously synchronized fashion.

AUTOMATIC BULB-BLOWING

The years after World War I saw startling gains in the making of glass bulbs for lamps. The Empire "F" and Westlake machines, constantly improved by technicians of General Electric and the glass companies, made practically all bulb-blowing automatic. These were rotary machines. As each machine revolved once it produced 12, 24, or 48 bulbs, depending on the number of blowing units in the mechanism. In the middle twenties it was possible to achieve an output of almost 5,000 bulbs per hour from a single machine of the most advanced type.

The process of drawing glass tubing became more efficient as the result of combining the Danner and Peiler machine developments. (See Chapter 12 for mention of the Danner machine.) Karl E. Peiler of the Hartford-Empire Co., a Corning enterprise, obtained a patent in 1926 on improvements in tube-drawing machinery. The Danner and Peiler ideas were combined in the final development known as the Danner-Peiler machine. General Electric invested about $400,000 in the perfecting of this machine over a period of several years. This work accounted for an increase from an original output of 2,000 pounds of tubing in 24 hours to a capacity of about 18,000 pounds.

Perhaps the most epochal advance in lamp-glass technology started in 1927, when Corning introduced an entirely new type of bulb-making unit—the ribbon machine. This extraordinary invention took a continuous ribbon of glass from the furnace and automatically blew bulbs in molds moving along a conveyor line that was part of the huge machine.

General Electric and Corning engineers improved the ribbon machine little by little over the next several years. Working steadily in the Glass Machine Works and the Glass Technology Laboratory, the General Electric specialists ironed out the "bugs" and stepped up the machine's capacity. Development was slow, and most of the excitement about it during these years was behind the scenes. The first ribbon machine placed in production by G.E. was not installed until 1933 and was not placed in full operation until 1934.

The machines that came out of this research were truly remarkable. They increased bulb output beyond the wildest estimates the glass experts could have imagined in 1925. A perfected ribbon machine could produce about 50,000 bulbs *per hour,* attended by an operator and several mechanics.

APPLICATION ENGINEERING

The lamps made by G.E. were more efficient than ever before. But it was not enough simply to turn out the best possible product. General Electric lamp men recognized their obligation to help customers use the lamps to best advantage. Furthermore, good application engineering has always been a valuable method of market development.

Illuminating engineering is a complicated science, largely because there's a good deal of art and physiology and psychology mixed up with the engineering. People instinctively like light, but not many are good judges of what kind of lighting will be most suitable for their needs. So illuminating engineers have to be especially cognizant of intangible factors.

At the same time, the physical horizons of their field keep moving farther along. Any conscientious lighting engineer will say, when pressed, something like this:

"Well, yes, we know a lot more about brightness and eye comfort and the mechanics of providing good illumination today than we did 10 years ago. We feel that we can prescribe very well for most lighting needs. But the more we learn, the more we realize that we haven't reached perfection. We get to know 98 out of 100 answers. Then we find that the number of questions just naturally expands to, let's say, 104. So we go ahead trying to close that perpetual little gap."

The fact remains that before the engineer can philosophize and explore the farther reaches of his subject, he must first have mastered the tools and the basic knowledge that have evolved over the years.

The lighting engineer's basic tool is the light meter—an instrument that measures the quantity of light falling on a surface or in a certain plane. Quantity of light is no more important than quality of lighting, but it usually comes first in the engineer's thinking because, to see at all, we must have a certain amount of light. Also, various seeing tasks require certain minimum amounts of light if we are to see comfortably and efficiently.

Light meters of many different kinds and sizes have been devised in the last 40 years. However, easily portable meters were much needed for a long time. Some of the first practical solutions for this need were developed by C. F. Sackett and his associates in the Nela Park Engineering Department in 1917. Following World War I these meters came into widespread use, were perfected further, and gave many an engineer "on the job" a means of determining lighting requirements. Chester L. Dows, an expert in lighting-engineering tests and standards, became known over his 40-year service in the Engineering Department as a first-class authority on these and many other measuring instruments.

One of the secrets of recommending good lighting successfully is demonstration. In 1919, as part of the Lighting Research Laboratory, demonstration rooms for residential lighting were set up at Nela Park. Today they would seem crude and old-fashioned, but for their time they represented the best in home lighting. They served to show people throughout the lighting industry what to suggest for the customer.

In 1920 Ward Harrison and Earl A. Anderson originated the lumen or room index method of general lighting design. This system of prescribing lighting took into account the proportions of the room to be lighted, the color of walls and ceiling, the distribution of light from various types of lighting fixtures, etc. The method Harrison and Anderson evolved greatly simplified procedure in lighting design and made the science much more exact.

To take the benefits of engineering research to the public, the Nela Park management established a magazine that combined several earlier publications. In May, 1923, the first issue of *Light Magazine* appeared. Roscoe E. Scott was the managing editor and John R. Colville the technical editor. The editor in chief was Dr. Charles A. Eaton, who had been active in industrial-relations work at Nela Park.

Dr. Eaton had filled several responsible positions as a writer and editor and had served as a clergyman in a leading Cleveland church. In late 1924, after leaving General Electric, he was elected to the House of Representatives from a New Jersey district. He served continuously in Congress for 28 years, winning acclaim for his leadership as the ranking Republican member of the House Foreign Affairs Committee.

Besides *Light Magazine,* the engineers found another way to tell the world about better lighting.

In the summer of 1923 they established the Nela School of Lighting in a building now known as the Advertising building. This was the forerunner of the G-E Lighting Institute, and it provided a training center for groups from all over the country: General Electric field representatives, sales agents at the wholesale and retail levels, utility executives and lighting specialists, architects, and consulting engineers.

Lee C. Kent headed this activity at Nela Park for more than 25 years and established one of the finest records of achievement ever known in the lighting industry. He was aided by a staff that changed frequently as its individual talents came into demand in other departments of the business, but always there was competent, smooth operation under Kent's direction.

At Harrison the Edison Lamp Works had also been working on a demonstration center to train salesmen and sell higher standards of illumination. Under George H. Stickney, manager of engineering, the Edison Lighting Institute was established with Arthur F. Loewe as director, and with the help of Alston Rodgers, A. S. Turner, Jr., Helen G. McKinlay, and Lillian Eddy among others.

National and Edison engineers turned out a profusion of engineering bulletins that informed the electrical trade and the public about the latest research findings and their practical applications. At Harrison these publications included contributions by such men as Alvin L. Powell, George H. Stickney, Henry Schroeder, Lawrence C. Porter, Arthur B. Oday, Oscar P. Anderson, and many others. Their opposite numbers at Nela Park kept the presses busy, too: Samuel Doane, Ward Harrison, George S. Merrill, Herbert Magdsick, Willard C. Brown, Walter Sturrock, and Charles E. Weitz come to mind as examples, though it would take much more space to name all the men whose studies were advancing the art of illuminating engineering. The engineering accomplishments of this period and later years made individual names unimportant.

Always important, and probably the most effective force in bringing better lighting to the public, were the nationwide staffs of National and Edison engineers, salesmen, and agents in the field. Backed by advertising that had made MAZDA a household word—synonymous with lamp bulbs—these people represented General Electric in the vital direct contacts with customers. The quality of their day-by-day work could often determine the company's progress in the lamp business. The record of consumer acceptance and sales proved that they were doing a superlative job.

CHAPTER 15

Final Steps toward Unified
Management

DURING THE YEARS 1912 to 1926 General Electric's agency
system of lamp sales had been functioning effectively. At
Harrison, George C. Osborne succeeded Adam Page as
sales manager of the Edison Lamp Works. Page moved to the
administrative offices of G.E. in New York City. Osborn was
assisted by Edwin E. Potter, Walter H. Thompson, and a nationwide sales staff.

At Nela Park, Joseph E. Kewley in the Administration Department headed all marketing activities from 1925 on. W. G. Mc-
Kitterick, as manager of the Sales Department, headed a strong
team in the home office, as well as more than 25 managers and
assistant managers in the divisional sales offices.

Albert S. Terry acted as supervisor, reviewing the lamp contracts concluded under the agency system. In this position he was
located at Harrison. Terry was a veteran of the lamp business,
having been secretary and treasurer of the Sunbeam Incandescent
Lamp Co. from 1892 until the formation of National.

In addition to the agency system, the "A" and "B" licensing
arrangements had been in successful operation since 1912. But in
1922 the lamp business was again involved in legal problems.

ANTITRUST PROCEEDINGS, 1922–1926

In 1922 a committee of the New York state legislature held a
series of hearings to determine whether the state's antitrust laws

were being violated. Lamp manufacturing was one of the industries about which the committee received complaints (in regard to patents, licensing, and the agency system).

During the hearings G.E. was not permitted by the committee to answer charges made against the company. So General Electric, to make its position and its practices perfectly clear, asked the Attorney General of the United States to investigate thoroughly.

If there were any doubts about the legality of its operations, the company wanted to clear them up and take any action necessary to assure conformance with the antitrust laws. The Attorney General had reviewed the agency plan at the time it was first put into effect. The Federal Trade Commission had also investigated the agency system in 1919 and had taken no action, indicating that the commission did not disapprove.

In its letter to the Attorney General in 1922, the General Electric Company said, in part:

"If the charges made are true, the General Electric Company is a violator of the Federal law and should be dealt with accordingly. If the charges are not true, while the Company has no legal redress, at least it should not be condemned by the American people.

"Inasmuch as these charges come directly under your jurisdiction, we invite you to investigate them, and if you are in doubt as to the legality of any of our acts, to bring an appropriate proceeding in a court where we may be heard, in order that the matter may be determined."

As a result of the company's request and the investigation that followed, the government filed a civil suit against G.E. and Westinghouse under the Sherman antitrust law. This was in late March, 1924.

The case was brought before the U.S. District Court for the Northern District of Ohio in Cleveland. After a full hearing, the court dismissed the case on April 3, 1925. This of course was a vindication for the company. The government then appealed to the Supreme Court. There the court's opinion, written by Chief Justice William Howard Taft, affirmed the action of the lower court. It stated that the license agreement between G.E. and

Westinghouse was entirely legal and that the agency system conformed fully to the law.

MANAGEMENT LEADERS

Changes in leadership naturally occurred from time to time at Nela Park and Harrison. In 1916 George Morrison had been elected to a G.E. vice-presidency. W. R. Burrows succeeded him as manager of the Edison Lamp Works. The administrative group working with Burrows included thoroughly experienced managers such as Frank W. Patterson, Henry B. Rogers, and Carl T. Fuller. Thomas J. McIntyre, attached to the Harrison headquarters, functioned as a liaison man between Edison and National. He was the secretary of the policy-making committees on which both groups were represented.

At Nela Park both F. S. Terry and B. G. Tremaine were looking toward retirement by 1921, and wanted to turn over the active management of National to other hands.

At the end of that year they set up an advisory board for over-all planning. Terry served as chairman and Tremaine as vice-chairman. T. W. Frech became National's general manager— the active top administrator of the business.

Other prominent figures in the Administration Department during the next few years were Leroy P. Sawyer, William H. Roberts, Dr. Zay Jeffries, Edwin Irving, and, as mentioned before, Joseph E. Kewley. In 1926 Sawyer moved to the G-E headquarters in New York City. Roberts headed all manufacturing, while Dr. Jeffries acted as consultant on major problems of research and development. William L. Enfield, who had succeeded John Randall as manager of the Lamp Development Laboratory, continued in that capacity.

In 1923 both Terry and Tremaine moved further toward less active participation in the day-to-day management. They were satisfied that Frech was handling his job in excellent fashion. Terry was named as a General Electric vice-president and Tremaine was elected to the company's board of directors. Mr. Tremaine continued as a director for 22 years, retiring in 1945 three years before his death at the age of 84. Terry, however, was not fortunate enough to see the later progress of the business he had done so much to establish. He died suddenly in 1926, but he had the satisfaction of knowing that the National management was continuing along the lines he had marked so clearly—business idealism, research, effective salesmanship, and the Authority Reserved method of management.

Meanwhile the top management of the General Electric Company had also changed. E. W. Rice, the brilliant technical director, became president upon the retirement of Charles Coffin in 1913, and guided the company through the difficult war years. In 1922 Gerard Swope took over the presidency and Owen D. Young became chairman of the board. Swope had worked, at $1 a day, as a helper in the G-E repair shop at the World's Fair in Chicago in 1893. This was during the summer between his second and third years at Massachusetts Institute of Technology. Later, with Western Electric, he rose through the ranks to become a vice-president. He moved to General Electric as president of the International General Electric Company a few years before his election to the top position in the parent company. In 1912 Coffin had persuaded Owen Young, an exceptionally gifted lawyer, to join the company as general counsel. In that post he was soon made a vice-president.

MOVING TOWARD CONSOLIDATION

As a new generation succeeded to the leadership of many departments in Edison and National, a gradual recognition of the need for consolidation developed. Within General Electric, the Edison and National managements were largely independent. Their friendly rivalry had its advantages and its handicaps. The two groups shared technical knowledge with each other. They met together in committees for joint planning. They grew to know and like each other in sessions on Association Island. But inevitably there was some duplication of effort and of facilities. It became apparent that a stronger, more efficient organization could be built by complete consolidation.

The statistics measuring growth in the lamp business kept going along an upward curve. The $57 million in total annual volume for all manufacturers in 1919 had expanded to about $73 million by 1925. From 224 million large lamps produced in 1919, the output reached 273 million six years later. Production of miniature lamps shot upward from 85 million in 1921 to 180 million in 1925.

The job of welding National and Edison into one organization with headquarters at Nela Park was a formidable one. It could not be accomplished immediately, nor even in one year. As it turned out, six years (1925–1931) were required before the many changes were finally completed.

THE NEW INCANDESCENT LAMP DEPARTMENT

The name chosen for the new combination was the Incandescent Lamp Department of General Electric. The manufacturing divisions—and those closely related to manufacturing—were brought together first. This was largely accomplished in 1925 and 1926, though not entirely finished until 1930.

In the fall of 1925 Frank W. Patterson moved from Harrison to Nela Park as associate manager of the Large Lamp Manufacturing Department. His co-manager was Martin L. Sloan, who had been in charge of the department since 1921. In July, 1927, Sloan joined W. H. Roberts in the Administration Department to aid in the direction of all manufacturing, while Patterson retained the job he and Sloan had previously shared.

Frank H. Blackburn, who had headed the Standardizing Department since 1915, transferred to New York City in 1927. The management of the Standardizing Department then passed to Carl T. Fuller, who had come to Nela Park in 1925 as associate manager.

As these early transitions took place, W. R. Burrows and T. W. Frech worked together to supervise the consolidation process. Their joint leadership continued from 1925 to 1927. Then Burrows proceeded to New York City as a General Electric vice-president in charge of a special manufacturing activity. Frech continued as general manager of the Incandescent Lamp Department and in 1931 was also named as the General Electric vice-president in charge.

As chief administrator, Frech showed a conspicuous devotion to the Authority Reserved system of business organization (see Chapter 10). Throughout the period of his managership from 1921 to 1934 he maintained the structure and the spirit of this unique idea. To make it clear to others—and perhaps especially for the benefit of the Edison men who were really experiencing the Authority Reserved system for the first time—Frech wrote a book describing the organizational structure and the business principles represented in it. Dr. Zay Jeffries assisted in the preparation of this volume.

It was a slim little book physically—only 63 printed pages. It carried no authors' names. The title page bore the inscription: "Printed but not published. Cleveland, Ohio, September, 1930." This meant that it was not for general distribution. Nowhere in its pages were the names of individuals used, nor the names of National or General Electric. The title was "Business Ideals, Principles, and Policies." Yet, for all its unpretentiousness, the book served a useful purpose by summarizing the methods that Terry had developed and that Frech was continuing to practice.

The consolidation of engineering, sales, and sales promotion developed more slowly than in manufacturing. The staffs in each of these fields were gradually fused into an efficient combination in the divisional offices throughout the country as well as at Nela Park.

One of the major developments was the assignment of illuminating engineers to the various sales divisions. This had been started on an experimental basis as early as 1920, when James M. Ketch of the Nela Park Engineering Department brought to customers in the South the ideas and methods developed in Cleveland. In 1923 Ketch became the engineer for the Michigan Division in Detroit. His work proved the value of closer contact between the consumer and the Engineering Department.

A complete line-up of division engineers was established in succeeding years. Their work grew into one of the most fruitful activities of the Lamp Department.

In 1930 Ward Harrison took over the management of the Engineering Department, succeeding S. E. Doane. This was another example of the "classes of 1909 to 1920" progressing to leadership as the pioneers of lampmaking began to play less active parts. Harrison was admirably suited to the intensive demands of the new era in illuminating engineering. Completely objective, deeply sincere, he never failed to search for and find the essential truths of lighting principles, let the chips fall where they might. Just as Doane had built the leading organization in this field by encouraging young talent, so Harrison made his influence felt throughout the lighting industry by his own work and that of his associates.

Then there was the Law Department. If any proof of the need for competent legal counsel had been lacking previously, the anti-trust case of 1922–1926 supplied it. At the same time, of course, the Law Department handled countless recurring problems that were important even though they had no direct bearing on court actions. Here also the Incandescent Lamp Department was fortunate in the caliber of the men on its staff. C. W. Appleton, manager from 1921 to 1926, was followed by Howard C. Couse, a lawyer of great integrity and of calm, judicious temperament.

Getting the millions of lamps to the right place at the right time was a big job and it was handled by the Transportation Department. Harvey N. Sibbald managed this activity until 1930, supervising the service to customers in every corner of the nation. When W. George Davis was appointed as manager, the name of the department was changed to Warehouse and Transportation. After two years Davis assumed the leadership of the newly organized Parts Manufacturing Department (wire, glass, etc.) and left the service functions in the able hands of M. J. Hamner.

The tasks of sales management had enlarged tremendously. On the other hand, there was a wealth of sales talent in the sales offices of both National and Edison, so it was a difficult problem to assign divisional and headquarters responsibilities. The method adopted earlier in some departments, with an Edison man and a National man sharing a single managership, had not proved very successful. In Sales, however, a workable solution was reached in 1931 by dividing the nationwide operation into two parts. N. H. Boynton took charge of Western Sales, while Edwin E. Potter handled Eastern Sales.

Boynton had led the Publicity Department (advertising and sales promotion) from 1912 to 1918. He managed the Buckeye Division for eight years and then returned to Nela Park, in charge of sales promotion from 1927 to 1931. Potter's long career with the Edison Works included the New York district managership from 1919 to 1924 and the position of assistant general sales manager at Harrison from 1924 to 1931. Boynton and Potter led their sales staffs in different ways, each suiting his administration to his own personality. Yet together they created a unity and drive among General Electric lamp salesmen unmatched anywhere else in the industry.

Consolidating the field sales staffs was of course a somewhat delicate job, and took about two years—1930 and 1931. However, it was accomplished successfully by carefully considering individual positions and the previous abilities of both Edison and National sales-district organizations.

The Sales Promotion Department assumed more importance, too, as sales volume and advertising budgets increased. New media such as radio were employed, along with an ever-growing use of newspapers and magazines. Between Boynton's two turns at the helm, P. B. Zimmerman had been the manager (1918–1927) for National. Then, in 1931, H. Freeman Barnes came to Nela Park from Harrison to direct the department. Barnes had started at the Edison Works as a lighting engineer in 1918. Three years later he transferred to the Publicity Department, which was headed by John W. McIver, and in 1928 became assistant manager. Known for his perpetual friendly smile and his flair for the dramatic in presenting the advantages of better lighting, Freeman Barnes soon made a prominent place for himself in bringing those benefits to the American people. Not long after his appointment he was joined by Robert P. Burrows as assistant manager. Burrows had served National in sales and management positions on the West Coast. He handled much of the departmental organizational job, so that the team of Barnes and Burrows came to be accepted like the team of Boynton and Potter and other such combinations in the Lamp Department.

All told, by the end of 1931 the movement was complete and the combined organization was functioning well. The employee list had reached a total of more than 8,600 men and women. About 1,300 were at Nela Park; the great majority were employed in the factories and offices from coast to coast.

BOOSTING EFFICIENCY

The period of consolidation saw new developments in lamps —the change to inside-frosted bulbs, for instance, and others that will be covered in Chapter 16. It was also a time for making customer service better on other counts.

A notable step in this direction was the simplified line of lamps, which was worked out in 1925. The so-called "bread-and-butter" lamps accounted for a very high percentage of total volume. These were the household sizes in the standard line of lamps—those used most often in homes. The Lamp Department settled on a single bulb shape for the simplified line and used it for six wattages: 15, 25, 40, 50, 60, and 100 watts. These replaced 45 different types and sizes formerly made as general-purpose bulbs.

This change benefited everyone. Agents at all levels of distribution found their stock, storage, and display problems eased immeasurably. Warehousing costs and manufacturing costs were cut, and that helped to bring about lower selling prices. Consumers benefited from the price reductions and had an easier choice to make in buying bulbs.

At about the same time General Electric simplified the packaging of lamps, using bulb wrappers (sleeves) that made handling and storage easier.

Beginning in 1926 the G-E monogram and the wattage and voltage ratings were etched on the ends of the bulbs; this system replaced the small paper stickers formerly used.

An improved warehouse program accompanied the consolidation. From 1927 to 1929 larger and better warehouses were established in seven principal centers of demand. Over the next

20 years this phase of the business grew to embrace 18 district warehouses and 19 auxiliary warehouses devoted exclusively to lamps: a total of 700,000 square feet with a capacity of 150 million lamps. Agents and consumers got quicker, more satisfactory service.

UNIFIED AND READY

With a completely unified management, the Incandescent Lamp Department was now ready to meet the challenges of the difficult depression years to come.

A new "A" license between General Electric and Westinghouse was concluded at a time when the earlier agreement was soon to expire. Westinghouse wished to continue the arrangement. The new license was effective Jan. 1, 1927, though the details were not finally agreed upon until the following year. The license provisions were similar in general to those of the earlier agreement.

Lamp production in General Electric plants improved steadily. Output of large lamps climbed to about 62 per man-hour in 1930 as compared to about 30 in 1925. (The figures refer to direct operating labor—those employees actively engaged in lamp production.) This doubling of productivity in five years was largely attributable to the amazing improvements in machines and methods, making the individual operator's job easier rather than more demanding.

The work of lampmaking, which had once been seasonal according to demand, had been spread out by the management to give practically year-round employment. Employees' take-home pay increased as production volume and sales went up.

The industry's total production of large lamps in 1931 reached 319 million, compared to 273 million in 1925. Miniature-lamp volume was down, however, reflecting the downward economic trend after 1929 in the automobile industry and other industries that comprised major customers for these lamps.

The public shared in the benefits of volume production. General Electric followed its long-standing policy of reducing lamp prices as lower costs of manufacture and distribution made it possible.

Together with higher efficiency in the product, the price decreases during the twenties effected good-sized reductions in the consumer's cost of light. Price changes during this 10-year period are shown in the accompanying table.

G-E Lamp Prices

	60-WATT	100-WATT
1920	$.45	$1.10
1921	.45	1.00
1922	.40	.75
1923	.37	.70
1924	.32	.55
1925	.32	.50
1926	.30	.43
1927	.25	.40
1928	.22	.35
1929	.20	.35

The announcement that two such groups as the Edison and National Lamp Works are to be joined together appears quite often in business news pages, but the reader seldom realizes the complexities of such a movement. After the six years of adjustment required in this case, General Electric still manufactured lamps identified as "Edison MAZDA" and "National MAZDA." But now there was a single cohesive organization of men and women working toward the same objectives.

PART FOUR

Better Light for Better Sight

CHAPTER 16

Lamps for a Thousand Uses

UNTIL THE LATE 1920's the lamp industry placed primary emphasis on improvement of the basic source of light—the standard lamp bulb. By that time the tungsten lamp had been modernized with tipless construction and inside frosting. Most of the major steps in improving its efficiency had been completed.

To be sure, there were many different lighting applications and General Electric manufactured many other types of lamps. It was a long list:

Clear glass and white bowl lamps
Daylight and colored lamps
Christmas-tree lamps
Miniature lamps used for automobile headlights, indicator lights, flashlights, and other applications
Spotlights and floodlights
Lamps used for medical and dental work
Lamps for photographic projection
Lamps for street and highway lighting
Lamps for railroad use
Aviation lamps

All these were variants from the standard line. Each fulfilled a special purpose for which engineering and manufacturing data had to be worked out.

Now a new development period began. Improvements in the design and manufacture of the standard bulbs continued, but in addition the development specialists of the G-E Lamp Department moved into new fields and designed entirely new types of lamps. The eyes of even the most restrained researchers gleamed with excitement as these novel ideas moved toward the production stage.

Seldom in the history of lamp research were so many new types developed as during the period when William L. Enfield was manager and Harold D. Blake technical director of the Lamp Development Laboratory. Enfield followed John Randall as manager and carried on the administrative work particularly. He left the direction of the development work to Harold Blake, who played a prominent part in so many projects that none of them can be singled out as his major interest or contribution to better lighting. Together they formed a most effective team, guiding the laboratory's group of research specialists through a series of great advances in creative development.

First, of course, there were the improvements in standard lamps. Over the years from 1926 on, General Electric technicians made some 20 advances in the design of these "bread-and-butter" bulbs. Similarly, the machine experts patented improvements in lampmaking equipment.

Every year the lamps grew stronger, more uniform, more efficient—better for the consumer, easier to manufacture. The improvements are not listed here, nor the inventors' names, because the details are too specialized for general interest.

It would be foolish to say that General Electric laboratory men, engineers, salesmen, and administrators did not make mistakes or suffer setbacks as they developed and marketed their products. Of course they did. Nevertheless this was a time of exceptional progress. The G-E lamps in use today are superior products because the men and women throughout the organization kept in mind that the constant aim of G-E lamp research is to make "G-E Lamps Stay Brighter Longer."

The story of improvements and new types that follows in this chapter specifies certain years when the developments occurred. These are usually the dates when the new products appeared on the market. The actual development work was done earlier, since it always takes considerable time to bring laboratory findings to the production line.

Also, where individuals have been credited with these discoveries, they would be the first to point out the essential *group*
character of the work. In almost all cases it takes more than one
person to produce a refinement or a new product.

THE COILED-COIL FILAMENT

In addition to the improvements in standard lamps that boosted
efficiency a little at a time—adding $\frac{1}{10}$ lumen per watt here and
$\frac{2}{10}$ lpw there—one major design change resulted in a sizable increase. This was the coiled-coil filament.

From the time of Langmuir's work on gas-filled lamps the
industry had known that coiling the filament made the lamps more
efficient. The filament wire was coiled around mandrels as one of
the last major steps in filament manufacture.

In 1917 B. L. Benbow, manager of the Cleveland Wire Works
(a part of National), had obtained a patent on coiling the wire
twice, to make what could be called a "coiled-coil" filament.
Double coiling had been used for some projection lamps. However,
its application to the smaller filaments used in standard lamps
presented numerous difficulties for years after Benbow obtained
his patent. Double coiling required very precise tolerances. Each
tiny coil had to be spaced perfectly so that current would not jump

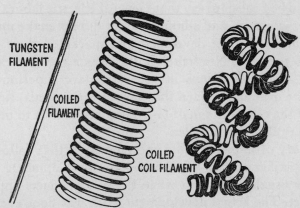

Comparison of a single-strand tungsten filament, a coiled filament, and a
coiled-coil filament (greatly enlarged).

from one coil to the next. There were problems in removing the mandrels or forms on which the wire was coiled. Experimental work went forward but it was not until the middle thirties that the Nela Park research workers and the Wire Works men could figure out completely practical methods for commercial production. Jonathan Force and John Flaws led this development work.

Introduced by General Electric in 1936, the coiled-coil filament accounted for a notable efficiency increase in standard lamps. The 60-watt lamp, for which the best previous rating was 12.5 lumens per watt, now reached 13.8 lpw, up a little more than 10 per cent. Output of the 100-watt lamp increased from 15.3 lpw to 16.0, a gain of about 4½ per cent.

ROUGH-SERVICE LAMPS

Most people think of lamp bulbs as being used in places where they sit firmly in their sockets and take relatively little abuse. But there are many other locations where lamps undergo severe punishment, where the tiny wires and glass parts take a beating from vibration and physical shock. A battleship needs light. So does a factory using heavy, high-speed machinery. The lamps are often mounted on the constantly vibrating machines. In thousands of locations it is handy to have a bulb on an extension cord, bringing the light to the work. The lamps in all such applications are subject to bumps or vibrations.

Years of experiment to design lamps that would withstand such treatment culminated in 1928 with General Electric's improved rough-service lamps. The filament wire was tightly coiled on very small mandrels. The relatively long coil was carefully mounted and held by many supports. (The 50-watt rough-service lamp, for example, has 16 supports.) Especially strong construction was used for the stem and other glass parts. Actually, two different types were developed—rough-service and vibration-service lamps —to fit special needs more closely. These types demonstrate the basic problem of all lampmaking—the creation of products able to take rough treatment, while the various parts are by nature delicate and precise.

PREFOCUS BASES

Robert S. Burnap of the Edison Lamp Works originated a method of base construction and filament positioning that made it possible to provide much more accurate distribution and concentration of light for certain special purposes. The prefocus base permitted placement of the filament very precisely with respect to reflecting surfaces and lenses. For instance, in a home movie projector there is usually a reflector behind the projection lamp to throw the light forward and a condensing lens in front of the lamp to concentrate the light on the screen. Burnap's design provided more effective filament positioning so that such reflectors and lenses could operate to best advantage. It was introduced in 1929, mostly for photographic projection lamps. Prefocus bases were applied successfully to automobile headlamps, beginning in 1933.

COPPER-TO-GLASS SEAL

For many years the factor that determined how large a lamp could be made was the strength of the glass-and-metal joints in the neck of the bulb. A very large lamp required a heavy filament and supporting structure. The size and weight of this assembly was limited by the relatively weak joining of glass to metal at the bottom of the bulb.

Daniel K. Wright of the Lamp Development Laboratory searched for a new method of combining an electrical conductor (copper) with an insulator (glass). His efforts finally led to a completely new internal structure for large-sized lamps. Wright was one of the Edison Lamp Works experts who had transferred to Nela Park in 1927.

The ingenious construction Dan Wright worked out was called a "bi-post base." Instead of mounting the filament on a glass support with the lead-in wires imbedded in the glass, he built up the internal structure from two heavy metal prongs (bi-posts). The prongs served as the lamp's base and as its electrical connections.

In assembly, the prongs were mounted in a jig; then a thick glass cup was sealed to them. A strong supporting structure, carrying the filament, was mounted on the prongs and the bulb was placed over the entire assembly and sealed to the glass cup.

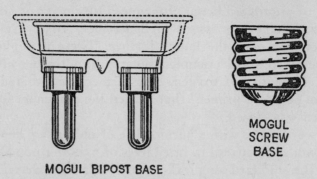

MOGUL BIPOST BASE

MOGUL
SCREW
BASE

This drawing shows how the bi-post base differs from the more familiar screw base.

First used in 1932 for large-sized motion-picture and airway lamps, bi-post construction was later employed for other applications, particularly automobile headlamps. Lamps could now be built to sizes of 10,000, 30,000, and even 50,000 watts. The mogul bi-post construction for these giants was later modified in medium bi-post lamps introduced in 1936. These included sizes from 500 watts to 1,500 watts inclusive.

PHOTOFLASH AND PHOTOFLOOD LAMPS

A new era in photography began in 1930 and 1931 when General Electric introduced photoflash lamps for the first time in the United States. The old cumbersome system of producing light for flash photography was to ignite flash powder on metal trays. It had always involved smoke, odor, and noise; the amount of light could not be accurately controlled. Now the amazing new bulbs soon replaced the earlier method. They produced a brilliant flash of white light, timed to the split second and synchronized with the camera shutter. There was no muss, no fuss, and the used bulbs were easily disposable. Photoflash lamps have revolutionized the art of pictorial news gathering. And, as everyone knows, amateurs use them by the millions for additional pleasure in photography.

General Electric purchased the American patent rights of the inventor of photoflash lamps, Johannes Ostermeier of Germany. The U.S. patent was issued in September, 1930. Nela Park specialists developed the lamps further. These first photoflash bulbs contained small crumpled squares of ultrathin aluminum foil and a quantity of oxygen. The filament was coated with a zirconium powder "primer" that ignited the aluminum foil when the switch was closed.

Here were lamps with a burning life of only a few hundredths of a second, as compared to rated lives of 750 or 1,000 hours for most of the standard lamps. To study their flash characteristics a new technique of photometric measurement had to be devised.

In 1932 G.E. introduced photoflood lamps. These had been developed by Gwilym F. Prideaux of the Nela Park Engineering Department. Photoflood bulbs produced high light intensities over a short life—3, 6, or 10 hours, according to size and type. They made possible much better picture-taking for both amateurs and professionals.

3-WATT ETCHED-FILAMENT LAMPS

About the same time that General Electric was building huge lamps ranging from 5,000 to 50,000 watts, an interesting new bulb appeared at the opposite end of the scale. It was a tiny lamp designed for use in clock dials, wall switches, and call signals in hospitals and hotels.

The filament wire was so thin as to be invisible to the naked eye. To produce wire that fine, tungsten had to be drawn through some 90 dies, many of them diamond dies. A small slug of tungsten less than ½ inch in diameter, when drawn in this manner, made a strand of wire 207 miles long—enough to supply filaments for more than 65,000 of these 3-watt lamps.

The last diamond die drew the wire to about $\frac{4}{10,000}$ inch in thickness. Then the wire was bathed in an acid that ate away part of the metal until the diameter decreased another $\frac{1}{10,000}$ inch. Finally it was washed, coiled, and cut into proper lengths for filaments.

These midget lamps, introduced in 1931, gave long-life service in 24-hour-per-day usage—another example of the unusual applications that called for resourceful design and manufacture.

FUSE WIRES IN LAMPS

Irving H. Van Horn of the Lamp Development Laboratory developed and perfected the use of fuse-wire construction in G-E lamps. One of the two lead-in wires was constructed to act as a fuse. It was thinner than the other wire. When the lamp burned out, the fuse wire opened the circuit automatically. This was an important safety measure, making violent failures of lamps almost impossible.

THREE-LIGHT LAMPS

One of the most useful types of lamps ever developed came on the market in 1933—the three-light lamp. These bulbs contained two filaments. One, for instance, might be a 100-watt filament and the other designed to operate on 200 watts. When used in conjunction with a multiple switch, the bulb could be turned to a lower level of light by using the 100-watt filament, to a medium level by using the 200-watt filament, and to a higher level by employing both filaments for a total of 300 watts.

Bulbs containing two filaments were not a new idea. Some had been manufactured many years before. But no one made them for general lighting service until General Electric figured out good applications for them in the early and middle 1930's. As a result, floor lamps, table lamps, and lighting fixtures were designed to utilize three-light bulbs. They brought added convenience, decorative beauty, and new ease of seeing to millions of American homes. These bulbs provided real flexibility in residential lighting, and manufacturers of portable lamps used them for literally millions of products in the next 20 years.

MECHANICAL BASES

Stronger and better bases were needed for high-wattage flood-lights and lamps used for street lighting. The same was true for some applications of general-service lamps. Severe operating conditions often subjected lamps to wide variations in temperature. In this rigorous service the cement used to seal the base to the bulb was affected. Weakening of the basing cement sometimes caused the failure of otherwise satisfactory lamps. Experts of the Lamp Development Laboratory and the Cleveland Equipment Works created a new type of base called the "mechanical base."

Introduced in 1933, the mechanical base did not use cement but, as the name implies, joined the bulb and the base in a structural conformation. The neck of the bulb was molded with four indentations or recesses. Then an inner brass shell, made with screw threads, was placed on the neck of the bulb. This brass collar had four lugs corresponding to the recesses in the glass, so that it snapped snugly into place. A regular large-sized (mogul) brass screw base was fitted to the inner shell. The result was a tight joint, with the necessary lead wires welded into proper contact. The lamps could stand up to great variations in temperature—freezing cold or the heat of long hours of service.

BETTER MEASURING INSTRUMENTS

Throughout the 1920–1940 period Nela Park workers continued to design improved measuring instruments—to check on the light output and general performance of all types of lamps, to measure illumination levels in any location, and to determine lighting needs in every conceivable application. It would be impossible to enumerate here all the devices built for these purposes. Only a few examples can be cited.

As one illustration, Dr. William E. Forsyth designed a very large and useful spectroscope. The instrument he constructed broke up a light beam into a spectrum; that, of course, is the major function of any spectroscope. But the Forsyth instrument also made it possible to select a single wavelength and to measure the power of the individual wavelength.

At about the same time—1933—a group in the Engineering Department developed a pocket-sized light meter. This brought to the highest degree of convenience the industry trend toward small portable meters for measuring illumination levels on the job. It was not easy. Building a high degree of accuracy, stability, and sturdiness into a small instrument is difficult even when a selling price of $50 to $100 is feasible. To accomplish similar results at a price of $11.50 was a tough job. But it was done, and the small G-E light meter, like those produced by other manufacturers, became an immensely useful tool for the lighting engineer.

The visibility meter, an instrument for appraising the relative visibility of various "seeing tasks," was made available in 1935. This meter was developed by Dr. Matthew Luckiesh and Frank K. Moss of the Lighting Research Laboratory. Where the light meter measured lighting levels, the visibility meter indicated lighting needs. An engineer could use it to determine many of the seeing problems of a typist, an industrial machine operator, or any other worker. It could measure the visibility of a store display, for example, or a traffic sign, so that better lighting could be prescribed.

IMPROVED PROJECTION LAMPS

A new line of projection lamps (for projecting movies or still pictures) appeared in 1933. They employed intricate, highly concentrated filaments, with several coils used together in two staggered rows. This was called biplane construction. It presented almost a solid rectangle of light, which provided much higher screen brightnesses—about double the levels attained before. Less bulb blackening permitted higher brightness to be maintained through the life of the lamp. Higher wattage in a bulb of a given physical size was possible, as compared to previous projection lamps.

LUMILINE LAMPS

In 1934 General Electric placed the lumiline lamp on the market. It was a tubular incandescent-light source with electrical contacts at each end. A long filament ran through the lamp, resting on a series of supports and providing a practically continuous line of light.

These lamps were 1 inch in diameter and were manufactured in three wattages. The 15-watt and 30-watt lamps were 18 inches long; the 40-watt lamp was 12 inches long. Later a 60-watt 18-inch lamp was supplied.

While lumiline lamps filled some utilitarian needs, they were especially well adapted to decorative lighting. G.E. made them available in clear glass, white inside-frosted glass, and a number of color coatings. They found uses in homes and in commercial applications, such as interior signs, coves, coffers, and showcases. Most of the development work on these lamps was accomplished by Paul O. Cartun of the Lamp Development Laboratory.

LENS-END FLASHLIGHT BULBS

Improvements in miniature lamps kept pace with the betterment of large lamps. For instance, there was the application of lens-end bulbs to the flashlight field. Bulbs with small built-in lenses had formerly been used only in such medical instruments as the bronchoscope, where they materially aided the work of physicians and surgeons. The diminutive bulbs for these purposes cost about a dollar each; they were especially made by hand.

Then Walter J. Geiger and Alfred T. Gaskill of the Lamp Development Laboratory developed a machine that would form these bulbs automatically. The cost per lamp dropped sharply, so that they could be sold for about 10 cents. This design achievement spurred the production of a single-cell flashlight only about 3 inches long and ⅝ inch in diameter. Soon afterward a similar two-cell light came along, known as the "fountain-pen" flashlight. The lens-end miniature lamps, which were introduced in 1934, supplied useful built-in light for many other small devices.

MULTIPLE CHRISTMAS-TREE LAMPS

The year 1934 saw a further real advance in small bulbs when General Electric made multiple Christmas-tree lamps available. Bulbs for the family Yule tree had formerly been made for operation in series only. When one lamp on a "string" burned out, they all went off until the burned-out bulb had been located and replaced. The new lamps operated on the multiple or parallel system, so that only the burned-out bulb ceased to operate. It could be spotted quickly and readily replaced.

GLASS MACHINERY IMPROVEMENTS

As stated earlier, by 1934 General Electric had in operation its first ribbon machine for bulbmaking. This installation was at the Pitney Glass Works in Cleveland. Within four years G-E technicians in glass machinery development increased the capacity of this type of machine from about 350,000 bulbs per 24 hours to about 900,000. Later they pushed this figure even higher—to about 1,250,000 bulbs every 24 hours. These gains came through successive improvements, through keeping everlastingly at the job of making the machines better. The Westlake type of machine, which was still used for much of the bulb output, was also further improved.

SILVERED-BOWL LAMPS

Silvered-bowl lamps joined the industry's parade of new types in the middle thirties. These were standard bulbs with a silver coating on the outside of the bowl (the lower part of the bulb). Other metallic coatings were also applied to "seal in" the silver finish. The Silvray Company pioneered the development of these lamps. The bowl coating shielded the bright filament from view and at the same time formed an efficient reflector, throwing light upward for indirect illumination.

Used in homes, schools, offices, and stores, silvered-bowl lamps filled a multitude of needs. Made in a wide range of sizes from 60 to 1,000 watts inclusive, they furnished a new reflector with each lamp replacement. This reduced the maintenance problems caused by the collection of dust and dirt on reflecting surfaces.

NEW REFLECTOR-LAMP DESIGNS

Another line of lamps with a built-in reflecting surface solved several lighting problems very satisfactorily. Known as reflector lamps, they were made in shapes that would help to concentrate the light as needed for spotlighting or floodlighting. An inside coating of vaporized aluminum, developed by Royal Strickland of G.E., was their most distinctive feature; it provided a highly efficient reflecting surface. The filament could be positioned for accurate control of the light, and the degree of frosting on the inside front surface of the glass helped to make the distribution pattern a "spot" or a "flood," as desired.

These R-bulb lamps served admirably for display lighting in stores, for many industrial applications, and for illumination of yards, gardens, and driveways. General Electric first listed them in 1936 in 150-watt and 300-watt sizes, with a 5-inch diameter. Later other sizes were added to the line.

ADVANCING BEYOND THE CARBON ARC

During this period General Electric also took rapid strides in developing lamps other than incandescent bulbs. The old carbon-arc lamp was surpassed as a general lighting source by the incandescent bulb. However, other useful lamps had been created from time to time that were essentially arc lamps.

So far this story of G-E lamps has concentrated on the incandescent developments. Now it is in order to review briefly some of the early arc lamps that differed from the carbon arc.

In the 1890's an inventor named D. M. Moore created light sources that were tubes many feet long and about 2 inches in diameter. The application of very high voltage (as high as 16,000 volts) caused an arc to strike through the long glass tube between the electrodes placed at each end. The tube was filled with gas. Nitrogen was used for some types of Moore tubes, carbon dioxide or ordinary air at very low pressures for others.

Moore, a G-E employee, left the company in 1894 and organized his own firm. The efficiency of the tubes was high and he found ways to obtain satisfactory lamp life. However, there were many handicaps of cost, complicated installation, high voltage, and difficult operation. The advent of tungsten-filament lamps caused Moore's business to decline. He sold it to General Electric in 1912 and resumed his work as a member of the laboratory staff in Schenectady.

THE COOPER-HEWITT LAMP

Meantime another electric-discharge lamp appeared. It was the mercury-vapor arc lamp introduced in 1901 by Peter Cooper Hewitt. Known as the Cooper-Hewitt lamp, it was the product of experiments the inventor made in Newark, N.J., following up the earlier work of nineteenth-century European researchers.

The Cooper-Hewitt lamp, 4 feet long, contained a small amount of mercury which was partially vaporized when electric current was applied to the electrodes at each end of the tube. Gradually an arc struck through the length of the tube and the result was production of a greenish-blue light.

Efficiency was high as compared to other light sources of that time—about 12.5 lumens per watt. Lamp life, about 2,000 hours, was very satisfactory. Because of the color quality of the light, however, the lamp was not suitable for general commercial use. Its most extensive application over the years was in industry, photography, and similar fields where the lack of red color components in the light was not especially important.

Besides the standard 4-foot, 385-watt lamp, Hewitt developed other sizes, but they were less widely used. The Cooper-Hewitt Electric Co., formed in 1902 with the financial support of George Westinghouse, promised to capture a good-sized slice of the lighting market. In time it did so, but its early years were marked by patent conflicts.

In the G-E Research Laboratory at Schenectady, Dr. Ezekiel Weintraub had invented a mercury-arc rectifier which converted alternating current to direct current. His colleague, Charles P. Steinmetz, designed a mercury-arc lamp that operated in conjunction with Weintraub's rectifier. The patent application for the General Electric rectifier came into conflict with a patent held by Hewitt for the same type of device. The question of priority remained unsettled.

For several years both companies were handicapped by this uncertainty. Finally, in 1913, an agreement involving the exchange of patent licenses permitted both to manufacture mercury-arc rectifiers and lamps freely. Then in 1919 General Electric purchased the Cooper-Hewitt company. It later became known as the General Electric Vapor Lamp Co., a G-E subsidiary.

During the period 1919–1940, Cooper-Hewitt lamps were improved and their operation was simplified. The Vapor Lamp Co. grew to be an influential factor, especially in industrial lighting. Its technical experts, engineers, and salesmen contributed much to the building of a better-lighted America.

Several other types of lamps operate on the same basic principle as the old Cooper-Hewitt lamp. A current will pass between electrodes sealed into a glass envelope that contains vapors or inert gases. Such a lamp may be called an "arc lamp" in the broad sense of the term. The action by which the current flows through the lamp and results in the production of light is called gaseous conduction.

All arc lamps require separate auxiliary equipment for satisfactory starting and consistent operation. The starting equipment aids in causing the arc to strike. The ballast governs the flow of current to assure normal, satisfactory operation.

THE S-1 SUNLAMP

One of the first fruits of General Electric work in electric-discharge lamps during the 1920's was not primarily a light source. It was the S-1 sunlamp. This was the first "lamp bulb" generating ultraviolet rays for the purpose of "sun-tanning" the skin. Earlier sunlamps had not resembled conventional lamp bulbs in appearance.

The S-1 lamp was a mercury-vapor type, producing both ultra-violet radiation and some visible light. A special glass bulb was used to screen out harmful rays. G.E. introduced it in 1929.

SODIUM-VAPOR LAMPS

For several years scientists in the Schenectady laboratory experimented with sodium vapor as the filling for electric-discharge lamps. They produced lamps that operated with an efficiency three to four times that of filament bulbs. However, the high efficiency could be maintained for only a few hours. The hot sodium vapor attacked any glass then available and blackened the bulbs very rapidly.

Finally, developments in glass technology produced a glass that would resist the effects of the heated sodium vapor. Lamps using this gaseous filling soon appeared in both Europe and the United States. From 1933 on General Electric made these lamps available. Producing a yellowish light, they were truly high-efficiency lamps (45 to 55 lumens per watt). They were (and are) used primarily for street and highway lighting.

MERCURY LAMPS

In 1934 General Electric began the manufacture of an important line of light sources for industry—high-intensity mercury lamps. They were produced by the Vapor Lamp Co. and marketed by the Lamp Department. First made in the 400-watt size, these Type H lamps did such an effective job that other sizes soon were made to fill out the line: 100, 250, and 3,000 watts. They could be used alone or combined with incandescent bulbs to provide more of a white color than could be obtained with the bluish mercury color alone.

These were intricate examples of lampmaking skill. An inner arc tube of quartz contained the electrodes (made of coiled tungsten wire) and several other small but important parts. A small amount of pure argon gas (to facilitate starting) and a minute, carefully measured amount of mercury provided the gas components. The mercury was vaporized by the heat resulting from the striking of the arc through the argon. The quartz arc tube was surrounded by an elongated glass bulb. The first 400-watt lamp was 13 inches long over all, including the base. Its diameter was 2 inches. More recently a shorter version has been manufactured, 11 inches long and slightly larger in diameter through most of its length.

COMBINED OPERATIONS

New types of lamps poured into the market, as the foregoing record shows. But important as the development work was, it served only as the starting point in a long series of demanding tasks in the General Electric Lamp Department.

In manufacturing there were literally hundreds of operating changes to be handled. Workers in the Equipment Works made contributions. So did those in the Base Works, the other parts plants, the glass factories, and in lamp-assembly operations. The Engineering group worked out the best applications for the new products. Sales Promotion—Sales—Service—Accounting—all divisions helped to provide the connecting links between the laboratories and the consuming public. A divisional sales manager in the South summed it up this way:

"New products in the early thirties gave us more opportunities to help our customers than we'd ever seen before. That was true even in the depths of the great business depression.

"Better lighting . . . better lamps . . . we've talked about them for years, until sometimes we feel like leaving the word 'better' out of our vocabularies entirely. But the customers didn't grow tired of hearing about more benefits for their homes or businesses. Furthermore, we can prove that our new products *are* better than what we were able to provide before—by actual measurement in most cases. We don't have to call a new lamp a

Super-Dynamic Ultra-Something-or-Other and trust that the fancy name will make it sound terrific.

"Anyway, at that time particularly—1930–1935—the public wanted more guidance. People wanted to know more about how to recognize their lighting needs. They welcomed good suggestions on how to fill those needs. And that's just what General Electric began to provide when it was wanted most. . . ."

CHAPTER 17

The Science of Seeing

EVERYONE WHO EXPERIENCED the world-wide business depression that began in 1929 remembers its devastating effects on the individual and on the nation. For several years the American economy struggled through a period of drastic deflation, with ravaging unemployment and sharp declines in production and national income.

The lamp industry was of course subject to the same forces of depression as all other business. Yet it weathered the economic hurricane with less severe ill effects than most industries. The sales record indicates the stability of the business even in the face of the economic crisis.

Sales (in Millions) of Large Tungsten-filament Lamps in the United States—Estimated by the Industry

1929	343	1934	379
1930	340	1935	413
1931	344	1936	462
1932	334	1937	506
1933	339		

Sales of miniature lamps and special types declined more than large lamps did during 1929–1933. But the public acceptance of the major products—now more than ever the "bread-and-butter" lamps—sustained the General Electric lamp business and kept employment at a relatively high level.

This was due in great measure to the sweat and spirit of the salesmen in every sales territory. They met the tough times with fortitude, persistence, and plain hard work. They sold G-E lamps when the salesmen in most lines, from locomotives to jelly beans, maintained that no one could or would buy anything.

The results of their work helped the entire electrical industry during the disheartening depression days. The employees in the Lamp Department factories naturally benefited, with a job security almost unmatched in American industry. General Electric lamp agents at the wholesale and retail levels found that their lamp business was a mainstay on which they could depend when other sales were slumping. The Lamp Department's energetic promotional work was advantageous to lighting-equipment manufacturers and to electric-light-and-power companies.

MANAGEMENT CHANGES

T. W. Frech retired as vice-president and general manager of the Lamp Department in 1934. His successor was Joseph E. Kewley. During Frech's leadership the successful consolidation of National and Edison had been effected. He had guided the organization through several years of rapid expansion, and it had met and overcome the most pressing difficulties of the depression. While Frech officially retired, his love for dealing with various problems in the lamp business persisted, along with his quiet friendliness toward all his coworkers. So he continued to appear regularly during the working week at Nela Park for some time —not interfering with the management he had relinquished but working on special projects that appealed to him.

J. E. Kewley had entered the company as a young lawyer in November, 1910, specializing in credit problems at first. He managed the Law Department at Nela Park for a little more than a year after World War I and in 1920 moved into the Administration Division as a top assistant to Frech. From 1925 to 1931 he headed all sales activity for National. A tall friendly man with a ready smile, he might best be described as rugged in both appearance and personality. Always a superior administrator, Kewley possessed an exceptional ability to help people compromise their differences beneficially in matters of policy and management.

During the decade 1930–1940 there were a number of retire-ments in the factories and the sales districts, with another well-trained generation of lamp men taking over management. New plants and district offices provided advancement for others.

At Nela Park there were relatively few changes in divisional management. M. J. Hamner continued to direct the General Service Division until 1936. Then he took up other administrative duties and in 1939 succeeded W. L. Enfield as manager of the Lamp Development Laboratory.

Following Carl Fuller as manager of the Standardizing Divi-sion was Raymond B. Walling, who served in that capacity during a busy 10 years from 1937 on.

In the Lamp Manufacturing Division, William J. Whiteside followed Frank Patterson. Whiteside began his managership in 1932. That was the year in which a new division—Parts Manu-facturing—was organized. Headed by W. George Davis, this group served all the factories making lamp parts, including (until 1941) the glass plants.

A new star in the management firmament emerged in 1934 when Philip D. Reed was appointed as manager of the Law Division, where he had first begun work with the company in 1926. This dynamic young lawyer made such an impression on top General Electric management that he soon found himself playing a pri-mary role in the over-all direction of the company. He was in charge of the Law Department for four years, then went on to assume further management responsibilities; and on Jan. 1, 1940, he was elected chairman of the board of General Electric. In 1938 Howard C. Couse was again named as the manager of the Law Division.

STUDYING THE PROCESS OF SEEING

Making and selling lamps was an interesting business. But what made it most engrossing was the fact that it involved studying *lighting* needs and problems—and that, in turn, required some understanding of *seeing*. For people buy lamps in order to get light, and they want light so that they can see.

However, this basic chain had not been very thoroughly understood or studied. It was so simple, when stated in its bare essentials, that most people—even those in the lighting industry—took it for granted. They had made great progress in the lighting art, but they found complications in obtaining satisfactory lighting for good seeing—psychological, physical, and engineering complications. Quite often lighting men became entangled in details (lumens, lamberts, cut-off angles, reflection factors, coefficients of utilization). These details were often quite important, but they were the trees. It wasn't until the late twenties and early thirties that people in the industry began to take a good over-all look at the forest.

Workers in the Lighting Research Laboratory at Nela Park reviewed the earlier studies of the subject and then took a different approach to the problems of seeing. They thoroughly explored the relationships between light and sight. This exhaustive research work was carried on under the direction of Dr. Matthew Luckiesh and Frank K. Moss. (The Lighting Research Laboratory was not the same as the Lamp Development Laboratory. One was concerned with the problems of people's lighting needs and possible solutions at the points where those needs existed; the other was concerned with improving existing lamps and developing new ones. There is always a meeting ground between these two types of research; they complement and help each other; but their day-by-day investigations are in rather different fields.)

How did various *quantities* of light affect the process of seeing? What were the effects of varying *quality* of lighting? How did human beings really see—was it by using the eyes and closely related bodily apparatus alone, or were other parts of the body involved and affected? These were some of the questions the Lighting Research Laboratory investigators asked themselves. Then they devised tests to determine the answers. Before drawing any conclusions they repeated each test time after time, using many people as subjects. In other words, their research was carried to points where its statistical validity could be firmly established.

For a good many years the Illuminating Engineering Society

had specified recommended lighting levels for various "seeing tasks" and various locations. These recommendations were made in terms of foot-candles. (A foot-candle is the measuring unit for lighting levels, just as the degree is the measuring unit for heat; the light meter is calibrated in foot-candles.) The Science of Seeing research now gave a more accurate and extensive basis for revised foot-candle recommendations.

RESEARCH FINDINGS

In many of the tests, reading was used as a seeing task. Books printed in normal reading type (10-point and 12-point sizes) were read by many individuals under 1, 10, and 100 foot-candles. Actually, it was *possible* for most people to read such print under very little illumination—less than 1 foot-candle—but this was very difficult and tiring over any considerable length of time. Also, no person could judge accurately for himself the relative difficulty or ease of seeing at various lighting levels. So Luckiesh and Moss and their assistants developed intricate apparatus to record mechanically or electrically such factors as nervous muscular tension and eye-muscle fatigue during the carefully controlled tests.

Here are some of the research findings, and some of the principles established in the Science of Seeing:

1. Visual acuity (sharpness of vision, or basic ability to see) increased about 30 per cent under 10 foot-candles of light as compared to 1 foot-candle. It increased about 70 per cent under 100 foot-candles as compared to 1 foot-candle.

2. Eye-muscle fatigue was much less when people read under 100 foot-candles than it was under 1 foot-candle. Certain eye muscles tired three times as much under the low level of illumination as under the high level.

3. Nervous muscular tension—a tension affecting the entire body during the work of seeing—decreased materially as the illumination level was raised.

4. It had long been known, of course, that the eyes, the optic nervous system, and the brain are all used in seeing. The new

research now indicated that the entire nervous system and muscular system is affected, that people are "human seeing machines."

5. Man has naturally grown accustomed over the centuries to the seeing conditions existing outdoors in nature. Now, however, people perform many demanding visual tasks indoors under low levels of lighting. This is much more difficult "seeing work" than occurs outdoors, where there are hundreds and even thousands of foot-candles of light from the sun.

6. As a result, eyesight defects have become common. They are not necessarily attributable to poor lighting, but certainly we are asking our eyes to do more difficult work than they did a few hundred years ago, before man moved indoors. The eye specialist can prescribe glasses, and they are very effective aids to seeing. But in addition, seeing can be made easier and eyesight conserved by providing more and better electric lighting.

7. Glare sharply reduces the ability to see. Therefore it is important to eliminate all forms of direct or reflected glare in order to obtain comfort and greater ability to see.

8. The same is true of heavy shadows and harsh contrasts. So it is essential not only to provide the quantities of light recommended for easy seeing, but to be sure also that the quality of lighting is right. Lighting quality is improved by such steps as the shading or shielding of light sources; avoidance of dark surroundings in contrast to bright spots of light on the work; good placement and control of the light from lamps and fixtures.

9. Factors that affect seeing include size—the size of the object or the work to be seen; brightness; contrast; and time—the length of time allowed for seeing or the time during which an individual is engaged in seeing tasks. All of these factors can be changed somewhat on occasion, so that better seeing will result. But the easiest one to change, and the factor most readily controlled, is brightness. For instance, the evening newspaper is printed with a size of type and on a kind of paper which do not make for easy reading. The chances of persuading the publishers to use 12-point type, and "slick" paper instead of newsprint, are rather slim; the costs would be prohibitive. But reading the paper can be made much less difficult if the lighting is increased to

recommended levels, with light that is free of glare, shadows, and harsh contrasts.

10. With the lighting industry well equipped to provide good illumination, there is no longer any reason to be handicapped by "barely seeing" when seeing can be made so much easier—in the home, the factory, the school, the store, and the office.

There was more—much more—to the research and information gathered together and called "the Science of Seeing." The Lighting Research Laboratory studies continued. But, as indicated by some of the foregoing points, a new approach had been found to studying and filling lighting needs. The Lamp Department now had the tools to do a better job of analysis and improvement. The new types of lamps played their parts as well.

The Science of Seeing opened wider fields for lighting engineers and salesmen. One could have the finest lamps to sell—and the best reasons in the world for selling them—but unless the facts could be brought to the public dramatically and thoroughly, there would still be apathy toward the problems of improving illumination. There would still be inadequate lighting in most locations. The United States needed a lighting education—and the G-E Lamp Department took on that part of the job, too, along with the rest of the lighting industry.

CHAPTER 18

The Lighting Education of a Nation

THE SCIENCE OF SEEING provided a core of sound ideas. Using that central fund of reasons for better lighting, the Lamp Department expanded its activities in every direction. There was a great ferment of lighting education and sales promotion. To those engaged in it there was more excitement, enjoyment, and conviction than they had ever before experienced in the lighting industry.

One of the personalities typifying this surge of enthusiasm was Freeman Barnes, manager of the Sales Promotion Division. Barnes could make an exceptionally warm, appealing presentation of Science of Seeing ideas on the platform before any group. Besides his sense of drama and timing, he had a sincere belief in helping people benefit through better seeing. So he led the movement that took to the industry and the public the concepts Dr. Luckiesh and his colleagues had worked out. Barnes toured the country speaking on the subject; he talked to groups assembled in the Lighting Institute at Nela Park; and he made his presentation into short, effective motion pictures that were widely distributed.

It is doubtful that any information program anywhere in industry has had a more effective, attention-compelling team of advocates than Barnes and Luckiesh as they operated from 1933 to 1941. And they were joined early in this program by a lively group of associates, not only at Nela Park but also in every Lamp Department territory.

THE INSTITUTE LEADS THE WAY

In 1933 the Lighting Institute was revitalized and enlarged with new displays, demonstrations, and meeting programs. Here was an attractive building with 22,000 square feet of floor space devoted to education in lighting. Its reputation as the center of such information became world-wide. Lighting experts from Europe, Asia, and South America came to learn more about their specialty. As for Americans, they came by the thousands every year—representatives of lighting-equipment manufacturers, of electric-light-and-power companies, of electrical wholesalers and retailers, plus other thousands from the general public. All were eager to get the latest ideas in lighting for homes, schools, stores, offices, and factories.

It was all in the day's work for L. C. Kent and his assistants to take care of several diverse groups of visitors, who might range from high-school students to engineers, architects, and designers specializing in highly complex problems. Each group found a full program scheduled. People from various sections at Nela Park gave demonstrations and talks of major interest to the particular audience involved, so that this work became an important part of the job for many members of the staff.

The walls of the Institute were lined with exhibits: demonstrations of Science of Seeing ideas; many types of G-E lamps; the history of lamps and lighting; and recommended installations of modern lighting. Besides a good-sized auditorium with a well-equipped stage, the building contained demonstration rooms where groups could meet to discuss the primary fields of lighting.

Even so, the men and women exploring the new approach to lighting were dissatisfied. They were more than happy with the job the Institute was doing, but, in addition to the thousands they were reaching in that way, they wanted to bring the Science of Seeing to an ever-widening circle of millions.

They put together several "traveling Institutes." Each one employed a team of Nela Park people and a truckload of demonstration materials. During 1934 these troupes were on the road for several months, bringing to hundreds of community meetings as much of the Institute as possible.

Many of the younger generation of that time at Nela Park won recognition as General Electric lighting leaders during these tours. This type of traveling demonstration had been used before by the Lamp Department, and has been employed since. It was not unique in American industry. But those who participated in the 1934 program still tell tales of the missionary zeal that sparked them, and agree that it marked a high point in their business lives. The story they had to tell involved the conservation of that most precious possession—eyesight. It came as close to true public education as any business message could.

There are many Americans today, of course, who have never heard of the Science of Seeing as such. But they have been exposed to parts of it in General Electric lamp advertising, in films, in meetings, in ordinary conversations. Their seeing is easier, their lives are richer, even though they may care nothing about the meaning of foot-candles or quality of lighting. No one should be expected to give three cheers for General Electric just because his lighting has improved and because his children have more comfortable seeing at study and at play. But the campaigners for the Science of Seeing from 1933 on are satisfied that they have made contributions to American life even after the motive of selling more G-E lamps has been discounted.

HOME-LIGHTING ACTIVITY

By the standards established in the early thirties, most American homes were still miserably lighted. Dad fell asleep over the evening newspaper not only because he had done a day's work but also because the dim light made his eyes tired. Mother found it impossible to get enough light for sewing. The youngsters complained about their homework. Having to study algebra and Latin was bad enough, they thought, but trying to do it in glare and shadows—that made life very difficult.

This was not news to the home-lighting experts at Nela Park.

They had worked on these problems before. Now, however, they had the means to achieve better residential lighting.

First, they carried on experimental work in the territories of several electric-light-and-power companies. They developed a pattern for presenting the information to the public and for training home-lighting personnel in the utility companies and among equipment dealers.

Following the successful results in these test areas, the same segments of the lighting industry all over the country were encouraged to do a similar job. Staffs of home-lighting advisors and supervisors were trained and put to work. Most of them were young women, but several utility companies employed staffs of men for this program. During the middle and late thirties the total number of home-lighting advisors reached more than 2,500.

They made calls on homes throughout their territories. This was a service maintained largely by the utility companies, with no obligation for their customers to buy anything. An advisor surveyed the lighting in the home. She pointed out simple changes that could be made at little or no cost to improve existing lamps and fixtures. She carried a demonstration kit packed with interesting gadgets illustrating Science of Seeing facts and showing the advantages of good illumination. Finally, she filled out a complete recommendation form indicating the lighting changes that would be beneficial in various rooms. The householder could tell what lamp bulbs, portable lamps, and fixtures were needed to provide cheerful, comfortable lighting.

In addition, the home-lighting advisors and supervisors gave talks and demonstrations to groups such as women's clubs and Parent-Teacher Associations. They worked with department-store lamp buyers and with electrical retailers and wholesalers to get the best residential-lighting equipment in stock. They talked with architects and builders to aid in the specification of better wiring and lighting in new or remodeled homes.

The Illuminating Engineering Society set up design specifications for portable lamps (floor and table lamps) that would do a superior lighting job. These were known as I.E.S. lamps and were made by many manufacturers. So long as a manufacturer constructed lamps that conformed to the I.E.S. design requirements, he could place an I.E.S. tag on each such lamp. This tag was the mark of a portable lamp designed for better lighting results; it guided consumers in making beneficial purchases of equipment. Many of these portables used three-light bulbs to provide flexible levels of illumination, and they contained glass diffusing bowls that softened and spread the light properly.

The improvements in American homes as a result of this nation-wide home-lighting activity were incalculable. Millions of I.E.S. lamps were sold. More millions of fixtures and existing lamps were modernized and fitted with the right-sized bulbs. New fixtures blossomed where the old ones were inadequate. People learned to appreciate the decorative beauty that light could add to their homes. They enjoyed more convenience and easier seeing in every home task or recreation.

Eugene W. Commery led this program as head of the residential-lighting section of the Engineering Division. As he applied the research knowledge and engineering data to home-lighting situations, Commery showed the rare trait of always seeing not only the immediate need but the other needs that would soon arise. In this sense, good lighting can be called evolutionary: one improvement begets others. Commery's able associates in this work became known from coast to coast as authorities on almost every lighting problem in the home. Prominent among them were Mary E. Webber and Helen McKinlay at Nela Park, and Lillian Eddy working in and around New York City. Today Commery and his staff regard the 1933–1935 period as pioneer days. They have advanced far beyond the lighting practice they developed then; methods and equipment have improved steadily in the intervening years. Yet the ground-breaking was stimulating because there was so much to be done and so many changes were vitally needed in the average home.

COMMERCIAL AND INDUSTRIAL LIGHTING

As in residential lighting, leaders at Nela Park and in the field applied Science of Seeing ideas to the other major provinces of illumination—store, office, school, and factory. The training of competent engineers and salesmen was a feature in this program also.

A small army of enthusiastic workers for better lighting assembled in training schools at the Institute and at outdoor camps during the summer on the spacious grounds of Nela Park. Besides Lamp Department men, they included electrical contractors and dealers, wholesalers, and representatives of the utilities and the lighting-equipment manufacturers. Also, as it had done in home lighting, General Electric sponsored a detailed, written training program. This was published by the Corporation Service Division of LaSalle Extension University, after being prepared jointly by LaSalle and the Lamp Department. Several thousand men and women completed the G-E–LaSalle training programs.

Lamp Department engineers worked through the Illuminating Engineering Society to advance the knowledge of the lighting art and to improve its practice. Their advice was frequently sought by such organizations as the Edison Electric Institute, the association of major electric-light-and-power companies. The I.E.S., in conjunction with the American Standards Association, brought out detailed standards for school, office, and industrial lighting. These studies represented the best thinking and research of the entire profession, those working for other companies as well as General Electric, and those in the colleges.

In the store field, lighting began not only to match other advances in merchandising but to open new ways to good business for large and small stores alike. The engineers made tests on the "stopping power" and selling power of window displays and interior displays. James M. Ketch of the Nela Park Engineering Division evolved a new idea to emphasize the need for better window lighting and the values it could provide. This he called "Three-second Selling," pointing out that a window display received attention from the average passer-by for only three seconds. During that fleeting time it must make a selling impression; it takes superior illumination, daytime or night, to capture attention and provoke buying interest. Later, Ketch worked out the Three A's of good store illumination—lighting for *attraction,* for *ap-*

praisal of merchandise, and for an effective selling *atmosphere*. These were implemented by a long series of specific designs and recommendations for every merchandising purpose, worked out by a dozen or more Lamp Department engineers.

Other, more specialized fields were not neglected. Architectural lighting, automotive, street and highway, street railway, and bus lighting, various types of offices and schoolrooms, railroads, aviation, lighting for photography in every form—all these and others received attention. The illumination in the average factory—from textiles to toothbrushes, from food-packing plants to foundries—was below par. The industrial-lighting men attacked the problem on all fronts.

Nela Park issued a wide assortment of useful engineering bulletins, usually the work of an individual or a group specializing in the field concerned.

To name the entire roster of Lamp Department engineers who shared in this great extension of commercial and industrial lighting would be rather boring even if it were possible to be all-inclusive. Many examples could be dredged up from memory of a remarkable list of achievements. Always there was Ward Harrison—leading, counseling, acting as guide and mentor in the Authority Reserved tradition. As chief lieutenants to Harrison during this period one remembers Willard C. Brown and Herbert H. Magdsick, among others.

It is perhaps enough to say that the Lamp Department engineer, whether one finds him at Nela Park or in Oscaloosa, is almost always a singularly self-effacing individual. A reporter for the trade press, trying to pry out a statement regarding a certain accomplishment, has a tough time getting "personality" into his story. "Now how about this job where you got 60 foot-candles on the work and cut down spoilage 28 per cent—how did you get rid of those machine shadows that had always prevented really good illumination?"

"Well," says the engineer, "that wasn't too much trouble. Actually, Bob Harris, the fixture salesman, figured out the proper spacings. I gave him a little help but he did the real work. And we had a good contractor. That's half the battle. Be sure to give this fellow Simonson credit when you write it up."

LIGHT MAGAZINE

As mentioned before, since 1923 the Lamp Department had been blessed with an excellent means of distributing information, *Light Magazine*. It had grown more and more influential since the day when T. W. Frech launched it, with Roscoe E. Scott as managing editor and Dr. Charles A. Eaton as editor in chief.

The publication described itself as "a magazine portraying current progress in the science, art, and business of lighting as seen from Nela Park."

During the first four years Scott set the tone of the magazine and did much of the spadework to assure its initial success. In 1928 Ralph W. Shenton took over as managing editor. He was in turn succeeded by J. L. Tugman three years later.

Early in 1932 the activity was transferred from the Sales Promotion Division to the Engineering Division. Like his predecessors, Tugman built the magazine's reader interest, circulation, and physical appearance. He served for 15 years as editor in chief.

From the beginning, the aim of the editors was to make every story qualify as genuine news before it could be accepted. There was no room for routine publicity puffs. Throughout the period of intensive lighting education it has familiarized engineers, salesmen, designers, architects, and businessmen generally with "the science, art, and business of lighting."

BETTER LIGHT BETTER SIGHT BUREAU

As a further means of forwarding lighting education, the Better Light Better Sight Bureau came into being in 1934. This nonprofit organization with headquarters in New York City was supported by General Electric, Westinghouse, and (a few years later) Sylvania Electric Products, Inc., together with the Edison Electric Institute.

In its statement of organization it was defined as "an educational program under the sponsorship of the electric and allied industries to foster a better understanding of the relationship of light and sight."

From the beginning the Bureau engaged in no commercial activities, and the same is true today. It carries on its work of distributing information about eyesight conservation and good lighting through committees representing the membership. It publishes the Better Light Better Sight *News,* a magazine issued six times a year; prepares study projects in the field of light and sight for school classes; and provides a wide range of informational materials on home, school, office, and industrial lighting.

ADVERTISING AND SALES PROMOTION

General Electric lamp advertising brought Science of Seeing facts to the public during 1930–1940 with a program unprecedented in the lighting industry. A high proportion of publication space and radio time was devoted to this information, as compared to straight selling of G-E lamps. It was an effective way to sell lamps because these instructive advertisements illustrated the many needs not ordinarily recognized.

About this time General Electric made "bulbsnatcher" a household word. It designates the individual who robs one electric socket of its bulb in order to fill another socket. The cure for this sinister malady, of course, is to keep a good supply of spare bulbs on hand, so that every socket can always be filled with a lamp of the right size and type.

During these years the other lamp manufacturers were, in their own ways, telling the world about the advances of good illumination. And all the lampmakers, including General Electric, were competing strenuously to sell their individual brands.

As the better lighting program moved ahead, the General Electric district offices were provided not only with district engineers but with sales-promotion specialists as well. The information in both fields could be applied in day-by-day contacts with customers. There was no gap between Nela Park and the individual district manager and the sales force who were General Electric personified to the customer. The Nela Park operations remained as services to the districts rather than avenues of command. "Better light for better sight" was rolling smoothly along. Everyone in the Lamp Department could happily agree that selling better *lighting* was the best way to sell *lamps*.

Meanwhile the development workers added more new products to the stream that had been flowing so steadily since 1930.

TYPE D LAMPS

One development of the early thirties was not mentioned in Chapter 16 because it was related to the need for accurate and thorough public information about lamps and lighting as discussed here.

About 1930 the American market began to be flooded with inferior bulbs made in Japan and exported to the United States. These bulbs were not bargains as compared to their General Electric counterparts. When the purchaser used such a lamp he often lost more than the price of the G-E lamp, in terms of the light he was paying for. The reasons for this were concerned with the over-all cost of light and with the life and light output of the lamps.

In 1932 the list price of a 60-watt standard inside-frosted G-E lamp was 20 cents. Its rated life was 1,000 hours. During that time it would use 60 kilowatt-hours of electricity. The average rate prevailing for current in 1932 was 5.6 cents per kilowatt-hour. So the 60-watt bulb would use $3.36 worth of electricity over its long life.

If one of the 60-watt Japanese bulbs then on the market were less efficient than the G-E lamp by even 6 per cent, the loss of light would pay the full purchase price of the General Electric lamp. If the Japanese bulb were inferior by 10 per cent, the loss in light would be equal to more than 33 cents, as compared to the G-E lamp price of 20 cents. And the great majority of the Japanese bulbs were lower in comparative quality by considerably more than 6 or even 10 per cent.

Even with the lower electrical rates we have today, lamps account for only 10 to 15 per cent of the total cost of light, depending on various conditions of service.

The purchasers of the inferior imported bulbs, and of some other low-quality bulbs that were being made in the United States at about the same time, were losing a fair-sized proportion of the light they were paying for. Even if such lamps had been distributed free, they would not have been bargains.

So the Lamp Department brought out a line of bulbs called Type D lamps. They were not MAZDA lamps. Each of four sizes sold for 10 cents—60-watt, 30-watt, 15-watt, and 7½-watt. They were made available to satisfy customers who preferred to pay only 10 cents for a lamp even though it did not represent the top quality of design and construction exemplified in MAZDA lamps. The rated life of the 30-watt and 60-watt Type D lamps was 500 hours; life of the 15-watt bulb was 750 hours, and of the 7½-watt lamp, 1,400 hours. These lamps were better values than the inferior bulbs selling at the same price.

General Electric carried on a campaign to show the public the false economy of buying lamps on the basis of price alone. Type D lamps never accounted for more than a very small percentage of the company's total sales of lamps in the indicated sizes. A few years later G.E. discontinued the Type D line.

NEW PHOTOFLASH LAMPS

The first midget flash bulb was developed and introduced by G.E. in 1939. Designated the No. 5, it revolutionized the picture-taking habits of the nation because of its convenience, its high light output, and its low cost. It greatly stimulated both amateur and professional photography indoors and out.

In 1936 American patents were issued on a European development in the photoflash-lamp field. This was a lamp using small wires composed of magnesium and aluminum as the material to be ignited inside the bulb.

One of the first showings of General Electric fluorescent lamps, at the New York World's Fair. At that time not many people realized that these lamps would captivate the interest of the people and become a major light source in home, office, store, factory, and school.

In a 1938 national magazine advertisement, General Electric announced two remarkable new lamps—the fluorescent lamp and the projector lamp. By this time advertisements of this character had become much more informative than the old-time "ads."

George Inman (at left) and Richard Thayer (right), both prominent in fluorescent-lamp development, are shown here examining one of the lamps.

Ward Harrison, who was for many years head of the G-E Lamp Engineering Department, was very influential in guiding the proper application of fluorescent lamps in many fields.

All types of G-E lamps are carefully tested. These are circline fluorescent lamps on the test racks, where their life, efficiency, and other qualities are measured.

Fluorescent lamps presented many new research and manufacturing problems, but long experience in lampmaking helped to solve them. Here William L. Enfield (left), former manager of the Lamp Development Laboratory, discusses the lamps with Philip J. Pritchard.

This young lady is holding a replica of Edison's first practical incandescent bulb. Alongside her is the largest lamp bulb in the world, rated at 75,000 watts. It was built by G.E. in 1954 to commemorate Light's Diamond Jubilee—the 75th anniversary of Edison's invention.

General Electric

now brings picture-takers the biggest advance in flash bulbs since G-E Midgets in 1939

G-E No. 5

NEW M2

GETS GOOD PICTURES up to 15 feet, color shots at
same distance as SM. No. 5 took one shot
above; M 2 got the other. Which is which?

EASIER-TO-USE. New pinless base for quick handling. Just push in; bulb seats securely; releases
easily. Low-cost adapters for present cameras.

FLASHES TWICE AS EASY! New filament, three times
thinner than a human hair and new primer
give sure-fire flashing, even on weak batteries.

SUPER-HANDY PACKAGE. Small pack of 12 (in units
of 4) fits in one hand. Bulbs pop out when
finger presses...for quick, easy use.

You can put your confidence in—

Advertisement announcing the M2 photoflash bulb, a 1953 development by General Electric
that made flash picture-taking easier, more convenient, and less costly than ever before
(*Saturday Evening Post,* Mar. 20, 1954).

Only two changes: G-E Light Conditioning – and the lady!

PLEASE look again — the only thing new about the kitchen on the right is General Electric Light Conditioning. But it's made a new woman of the lady!

No more working in her own light. No more shadows to fool her. No more strain on eyes and nerves. In her Light Conditioned kitchen she's got plenty of bright and cheerful light. And right where she needs it —

at *each* work area!

In contrast to the single ceiling fixture on the left, the Light Conditioning kitchen recipe she's using calls for *four* strategically located light sources — in the ceiling, over the range, over the sink and under the cabinets. It's easy to see into pots and pans. Easy to measure ingredients. Easy to see whether dishes are clean. This Light Conditioning recipe specifies:

IN CEILING — at least three 20-watt or two 25-watt fluorescent lamps, or a combination of 22-watt and 32-watt circline lamps.

OVER RANGE — a 25 or 40-watt fluorescent.

OVER SINK — two 25-watt fluorescent lamps.

UNDER CABINETS — use 20-watt fluorescent lamp for each 25″ to 30″ of work counter.

NOW, MORE VALUE with General Electric fluorescent lamps! Recent improvements make them more efficient, longer lasting, with better color and uniformity, less end-blackening. 40-watt, **$1.05** plus tax.

NEW OZONE LAMP removes odors, freshens air. For use only in special fixtures made by a number of manufacturers in many attractive styles. Ask your General Electric lamp dealer for more information.

COMPARE new, smaller G-E 150-watt lamp (right) with old size (left). For enclosing globe fixture in kitchen ceiling, small 150-watt G-E Kitchen-Lite (with new aluminum base) **20¢** plus tax.

FREE RECIPE BOOKLET. 22 Light Conditioning recipes. Specifies bulbs, types of fixtures, measurements. Write Lamp Div., General Electric Company, Department 166-HG, Nela Park, Cleveland 12, Ohio.

You can put your confidence in —

GENERAL ⊕ ELECTRIC

G.E. made good home lighting easier to plan and easier to obtain by such Light Conditioning sales promotion as this. The above advertisement appeared in 1953.

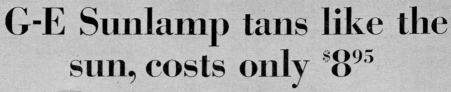

G-E Sunlamp tans like the sun, costs only $8⁹⁵

LOOK BETTER—MORE ATTRACTIVE ALL WINTER LONG

There's nothing like a tan to do wonders for your looks. A General Electric Sunlamp makes it easy to get one—right in your own home, and at low cost.

You get exactly the same kind of tan you get on the beach in the summer. You even get the same vitamin D the sun gives you. And think of the admiring looks you'll get. *Everyone* notices a tan!

Just put your G-E Sunlamp into any standard AC light socket, read the simple instruction booklet in the package, set the lamp the proper distance away from you and relax for the time specified.

A glowing tan can give your spirits a wonderful lift—especially during the cold, gray days of winter. Get your G-E Sunlamp and start your tan *today*.

LOOK FOR THE BEAUTIFUL G-E SUNLAMP GIRL ON THE PACKAGE —AT YOUR FAVORITE STORE

Accepted by Council of Physical Medicine and Rehabilitation of the American Medical Association

You can put your confidence in—

GENERAL GE ELECTRIC

Truly a long way from Edison's original bulbs, the G-E sunlamp brings easy sun-tanning to many. So popular has this charming picture of "Miss Sun-Tan" become that the advertisement has been repeated a number of times and her picture reproduced on sunlamp cartons.

Martin L. Sloan, general manager of the Lamp Department from 1942 to 1950 and a G-E vice-president during the last five years of that period.

Fred F. Harroff, vice-president of General Electric and general manager of the Lamp Department from 1950 to 1953.

Donald L. Millham, vice-president of General Electric and general manager of the Lamp Division from May, 1953.

The Wabash Appliance Corporation of Brooklyn, N.Y., took a license on this lamp from the owners of the patents. Wabash began to manufacture and market the product in 1936. (After World War II Sylvania Electric Products, Inc., purchased the Wabash company.)

Meantime the G-E experts in photolamps devised still another type, using finely shredded foil to provide the flash. These lamps, with improvements made during the next few years after their introduction (1940), became the type settled on by General Electric as the best in the photoflash field. They are made today in several sizes for various photographic requirements.

Also in 1940 General Electric placed flashtubes on the market. These were pioneered largely by Dr. Harold A. Edgerton of the Massachusetts Institute of Technology, with the cooperation of General Electric. Edward B. Noel did the development work at Nela Park. These tubes made it possible to "stop" fast action in sports, industrial, and military photographs. They produced tremendously brilliant flashes of light over time intervals ranging from $\frac{1}{1,000}$ to $\frac{1}{1,000,000}$ second. The same tubes could be flashed repeatedly, some of them at frequencies up to 10,000 flashes per second. They consisted of small-diameter glass or quartz tubing, either straight or helically coiled. Into the ends metal electrodes were sealed. The tubes were filled with a rare gas (usually xenon) through which an electrical discharge took place. Rather complicated auxiliary equipment had to be used with them. For this reason, and because of the relatively limited applications, flashtubes remained very specialized products but withal rather dazzling ones.

TUNGSTEN HEAT LAMPS

The Ford Motor Company had pioneered in the application of infrared lamps for radiant heating and drying. In 1938 General Electric marketed lamps of this type with tungsten filaments; earlier heat lamps had used carbon filaments. The use of tungsten assured greater economy because of longer life and higher overall efficiency.

Practically all lamps radiate both heat and light, and by far the greater percentage of radiation is in the infrared region. This radiant-heating effect is emphasized in the lamps for heating and drying. These lamps are designed for long life, with a sacrifice in light output because the lamps are not intended for the usual lighting purposes.

General Electric manufactured both clear-bulb and reflector types; the first lamps produced were in the 250-watt and 500-watt sizes. Now there are several sizes in each of three bulb shapes. Infrared bulbs have become extremely popular for many industrial uses. They are employed today in hundreds of factories and workshops for the rapid drying of finishes and similar uses. They have reduced drying time to minutes instead of hours. Production of scores of products has been speeded, improved in quality, and made less costly. Infrared lamps are being used in some cleaning plants to dry carpets and in laundries to dry blankets after washing, to cite only two examples of their versatility. They have also come into considerable use on the farm for poultry brooding and livestock care.

The 250-watt R-40 "red-end" heat lamp was designed for treatment of aches and pains whenever dry, penetrating heat was indicated as beneficial. It has become a standard item of equipment in many American homes.

PROJECTOR SPOT AND FLOOD LAMPS

One of the most significant new lines of G-E lamps came into production in 1938 when projector spot and flood lamps (PAR bulbs) were announced. Like the earlier reflector lamps, an efficient reflecting surface of aluminized hard glass was built in. Then a piece of pressed hard glass was joined to the reflecting surface. The hard glass, similar to that used in home baking dishes, formed the front surface of the lamp. Filaments could be positioned with great accuracy for maximum lighting results. The spot lamps had clear lenses, while the lenses for the flood lamps consisted of molded prisms in a pattern designed to produce the type of beam desired.

These lamps are used for show windows and interior displays in stores, for supplemental lighting in industry, for parking lots, gardens, and other outdoor applications. The 150-watt size was the first made, and the 200-watt and 300-watt sizes have since been added in the regular line.

ALL-GLASS SEALED-BEAM HEADLIGHTS

The greatest advance ever made in automobile headlighting was effected in 1939 and 1940. Sealed-beam headlights were developed over a considerable period through research by specialists of the Lamp Development Laboratory, Glass Works, and Engineering Division, working with the automobile manufacturers. They were a further application of the projector-lamp idea and the bi-post base.

General Electric made all-glass sealed-beam lamps. The Lamp Department technicians in glassworking deserve much credit for development of the lamps. In the laboratory, Dan Wright and Alfred Greiner were the leaders in sealed-beam development work. In the specially equipped automotive laboratory at Nela Park, a rigid and thorough testing program made the lamps prove their merits before they were approved for volume production.

Each lamp was a complete headlight unit with lens and reflector combined as in projector lamps. The reflector and the cover lens were molded separately and then sealed together during the lamp-assembly process. The aluminized reflector, hermetically sealed, could not tarnish. Dirt and moisture could not get in. The small input of electricity (40 watts) in comparison to the over-all lamp size (7-inch diameter) assured a high degree of maintenance of light over the life of the lamp. These features accounted for the slogan adopted for G-E all-glass sealed-beam lamps: "They *do not* grow dim."

No longer was there a hit-or-miss combination of separate bulb, reflector, and lens. No longer was the practical effect of the headlamps in driving unpredictable, as it had been, particularly as a car grew a little older and headlight bulbs had to be replaced. Here at last was a permanently focused and precisely designed beam pattern—a single unit with accuracy and efficiency permanently assured over the life of the lamp.

Getting the lamp designed, constructed, tested, and approved within the Lamp Department was a long, detailed process, calling for many talents. That is clear from the compressed foregoing description. But that was only part of the story. General Electric

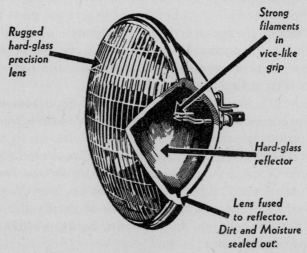

Rugged
hard-glass
precision
lens

Strong
filaments
in
vice-like
grip

Hard-glass
reflector

Lens fused
to reflector.
Dirt and Moisture
sealed out.

Cutaway view of the all-glass sealed-beam headlamp.

was satisfied that this was a vastly superior product. But how about the automobile industry and its intensely competitive manufacturers? How could universal acceptance of this radically new type of headlamp be obtained?

The lengthy negotiations to persuade the automobile manufacturers to adopt sealed-beam headlights on all new cars was a triumph for M. L. Sloan. At the time Sloan was assistant general manager of the Lamp Department, a position he had won in 1930. Now, in addition to his other duties, he took on this formidable job of diplomatic salesmanship, aided, of course, by Val J. Roper, Nela Park automotive-lighting engineer, and numerous G-E lamp salesmen working with the car manufacturers.

He worked for months, calmly and persistently, selling the sealed-beam idea, working out a multitude of details, never giving up despite a series of discouragements and many delicate conflicts of interest. Several companies in the automotive field developed sealed-beam lamps that were similar in design except that they used an inner bulb and reflecting surface of metal instead of glass, and employed a gasket between lens and reflector. Eventually Sloan's tireless endeavors brought about the specification of sealed-beam lamps by practically all the carmakers for their 1940 models. Some used all-glass lamps and others the glass-and-metal variety, but the change-over from the old style of headlights was practically complete and has remained in effect ever since.

Adaptor units were also made available, for older cars not equipped with sealed-beam lamps.

These headlights have been enormously important in increasing visibility and safety in night driving. Like the developments described earlier, these products that have helped to save lives demonstrated clearly the wisdom of expending $1½ to $2 million annually on General Electric lamp and lighting research.

Since 1940 the sealed-beam construction has been used for many varieties of G-E lamps. Here are some of them: marine lamps, signal lamps, fog lights, farm-tractor lights, airplane landing lamps, and bicycle lamps.

BRIGHTNESS METER

New instruments needed for accurate engineering work were developed, too. Among them was a brightness meter, light in weight and easy to handle, created by Dr. Matthew Luckiesh and A. H. Taylor, a physicist on the Lighting Research Laboratory staff. The engineers were recognizing more than ever the importance of controlling brightness—obtaining the needed foot-candles and yet maintaining and improving eye comfort.

MORE REDUCTIONS IN THE COST OF LIGHT

While the lighting education of the nation was proceeding, lamp production kept rising and the Lamp Department continued to reduce prices.

By 1939 the factories were turning out about 117 large lamps per man-hour (direct operating labor), as compared to about 62 in 1930. Automatic machinery was the major factor, with increases every year in the productivity of the lampmaking mechanisms. Far from reducing employment, this high efficiency and the greater demand for lamps provided more job opportunities. The

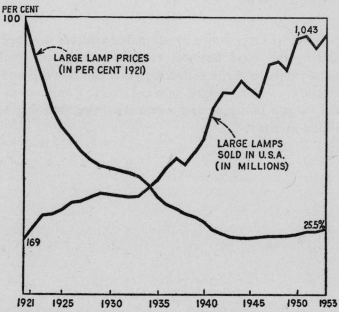

The chart shows how the reduction in lamp prices over the years stimulated the use of more and more lamps.

Lamp Department payrolls in 1930 included 8,620 men and women; in 1940 the figure was 10,846, and they were continuing to make steady gains in their take-home pay.

General Electric continued to reduce the prices of its lamps. The table on page 191 shows the trend for 100-watt and 60-watt standard lamps, carrying on the price information given about these bulbs in earlier chapters. Other types and sizes were also reduced in price at regular intervals, whenever savings and costs permitted.

Prices of Standard Incandescent Lamps

	100-WATT	60-WATT
1932	$.35	$.20
1933	.25	.20
1935	.20	.15
1938	.15	.15
1940	.15	.13
1942	.15	.10

Total sales of large lamps by all manufacturers dropped some-what during the 1938 business recession, from 506 million in 1937 to 487 million in the following year. But this dip was minor and temporary. Sales edged upward to 533 million in 1939, mounted to 593 in 1940, and zoomed to the amazing total of 726 million in 1941.

CHAPTER 19

The Magic of Fluorescence

ANOTHER GREAT ADVENTURE in lighting progress began at
Nela Park in 1934 and reached its climax within the next
four years: General Electric physicists, chemists, and engineers developed the fluorescent lamp.

This marvelous new light source seemed at first like a magic
wand, and indeed it has proved to be just that in revolutionizing
the art of lighting. In a relatively short time fluorescent lamps have
become a familiar sight to everyone. However, few of the millions
of people who use them know the inside story of how they work
and how General Electric developed them.

MAIN ELEMENTS OF DESIGN AND OPERATION

The fluorescent tube belongs basically to the family of lamps
called electric-discharge light sources, several of which were described in Chapter 16. At each end of the glass tube there is an
electrode. There is no direct connection between the electrodes—
no wire running through the tube from one end to the other.

The electrodes are small, coiled tungsten filaments with an
oxide coating on the filament wire. The tube contains a tiny drop
of mercury and a small amount of argon gas. As current is applied
the mercury is vaporized and an electric arc strikes through the
lamp. The mercury vapor thus becomes the connecting medium
through which the electric current flows from one electrode to
the other. The argon gas is present chiefly to aid in starting the arc
during the brief period required for the mercury to vaporize.

The mercury arc produces ultraviolet energy, concentrated in one particular wavelength (2,537 Angstrom units) which is invisible.

Finally, to transform the invisible ultraviolet into visible light, the inside of the glass tube is coated with phosphors. These are extremely small chemical particles in powder form which glow or fluoresce under the ultraviolet radiation. As a result, the tube glows with soft, abundant light.

It can be said, then, that there is a double conversion of energy in a fluorescent lamp—from electric current to ultraviolet, and from ultraviolet radiation to visible light. This is accomplished with high efficiency, so that the light output of fluorescent lamps is high in comparison with incandescent bulbs of equivalent wattage.

The size of the phosphor particles is important to good production of light and good appearance of the tube. They are really *very* small, ranging from about $\frac{1}{10,000}$ to $\frac{4}{10,000}$ inch in diameter. The total weight of the coating for the inside of a 40-watt white lamp 4 feet long is about $\frac{1}{10}$ ounce. So the science of applying the best phosphors is truly an exercise in delicate weights and measures.

As is usual with electric-discharge light sources, some auxiliary equipment is necessary for fluorescent lamp operation, in the form of starters and ballasts. (In recent years G.E. has developed some special kinds of fluorescent lamps with instant-start and rapid-start ballasts, for which no separate starters are needed.) The starter simply helps the arc to strike. The ballast controls the flow of current through the lamp. It consumes some wattage in addition to the lamp wattage; the amount varies with the type of lamp and type of ballast, but a fair average is 20 to 25 per cent of the lamp wattage.

THE DEVELOPMENT STORY

The first active work at Nela Park on fluorescent-lamp development started in November, 1934. There had been some earlier experimental work in this direction, using ultraviolet sources—for instance, attempts to improve the color quality of high-intensity mercury lamps by using various fluorescent materials.

Also for many years General Electric researchers had experimented with fluorescent materials. One was Dr. E. F. Nichols, who made some explorations along this line prior to 1924. Another was Dr. W. S. Andrews of Schenectady; his work with fluorescent substances dated back to 1912 and earlier. Research men at the G-E Vapor Lamp Company in Hoboken had made lamps of the Cooper-Hewitt type utilizing uranium glass, and these experimental products showed considerable fluorescence. In the 1920's Dr. Langmuir spent some time studying the action of electric-discharge tubes, with particular attention to low-pressure devices. At about the same time Dr. Albert W. Hull of the Schenectady laboratory worked along similar lines with low-pressure mercury-vapor lamps and rectifiers. On Jan. 27, 1931, he obtained a patent describing the results of this work. The Hull patent later assumed considerable importance in establishing General Electric's priority in fluorescent-lamp improvement.

The efforts of the men in the Lamp Development Laboratory received a strong impetus from a letter written by Dr. Arthur H. Compton on Oct. 27, 1934. Dr. Compton, the famous Nobel prize winner (he shared the prize in physics in 1927) was at that time retained as a technical consultant by General Electric. He was in Oxford, England, when he wrote the letter to Dr. William L. Enfield. Dr. Compton stated that the research experts of one of the English lamp companies he visited had shown him an interesting experimental lamp. It was tubular and the central portion was coated with fluorescent material. He expressed great interest in this as a field for exploration in lamp research. The letter gave no details as to current, dimensions, wattage, temperature, or phosphors. The British lamp emitted a yellowish-green light from the coated portion, and that area of the tube appeared to be highly efficient in light output.

This report fitted in with previous General Electric knowledge and served as an incentive for intensive experiment, but certainly there were a hundred details lacking. They would have to be painstakingly figured out before any new lamp of this type could be produced even in the laboratory.

Under the over-all management and counsel of Dr. Enfield, George E. Inman directed the project and took an active part in the development work. In the early stages, his group consisted of three men—Richard Thayer, Eugene Lemmers, and Dr. Willard A. Roberts. As the development progressed, more people participated, either as members of this group or in other departments.

In December the original group made a lamp of their own design, 10 inches long and about ¾ inch in diameter, with an electrode in each end. They used various phosphors then available, including zinc silicate. The results were encouraging enough to persuade them to continue their work. Early in 1935 they learned that one of the German lamp companies was also working along similar lines.

As with many inventions, the necessary individual factors for producing an efficient fluorescent lamp were being found, or had already been worked out, by a few individuals in several countries. But no completely practical lamp had yet been produced. Most of the information was not available in any one place. The General Electric men went ahead, figuring it out for themselves.

Balancing the various design factors was far from easy. The following quotation from an Engineering Division publication indicates the complexities:

"Within the range of acceptable bulb sizes, the designer (of fluorescent lamps) must compose the electrical characteristics to produce the desired lumens per foot, brightness per square inch of tube, and over-all efficiency. He must adjust the electrical relationship of current, voltage, lamp loading (which is the wattage-diameter-length relationship), and related gas pressures so as to provide reliable starting and satisfactory regulation under operating conditions as to temperature and humidity."

The engineers said quite a mouthful in those two sentences. The experiments and the guide charts that had to be worked out to show these variable design relationships were complicated, to use a bit of understatement. They required many days of careful work. The process was quite different from the cut-and-try methods used in the nineteenth century, which still often represent the public's idea of how modern inventions are made.

Besides the group in the Lamp Development Laboratory (LDL), other divisions of the Lamp Department and other branches of the General Electric Company contributed to the final creation of successful fluorescent lighting.

On many of these problems, the researches of Dr. Clifton G. Found, first at the Schenectady Research Laboratory and later at the Lamp Development Laboratory at Cleveland, cast much helpful light.

Dr. Willard Roberts, a chemist in the Lamp Development Laboratory, devoted a tremendous amount of work to the creation and selection of suitable fluorescent materials. Dr. G. R. Fonda and C. A. Nickel of Schenectady and Harry M. Fernberger of the Wire Division also aided in this part of the project. In the first few years of fluorescent-lamp production, the most important phosphors used were zinc beryllium silicate and magnesium tungstate, though numerous others were employed.

As the search progressed over a 10-year period, hundreds and hundreds of different materials were made up in sample batches and tested by Roberts and his associates. There are now more than 10,000 known fluorescent materials.

As the time for factory production approached, the staff of the Lamp Facilities Laboratory started the development of machinery for the purpose. This was in July, 1936. Philip J. Pritchard was in charge. As usual he accomplished so much in a comparatively short time that he rightfully received much of the credit for actually bringing these lamps into production.

This task involved new methods and different machine construction. There were few precedents to follow. A new lamp could be created in the laboratory but it could not be successfully mass-produced until the production specialists contrived practical methods for use in the factories. For instance, the early lamps designed in the Lamp Development Laboratory operated on an instant-start principle and had only one contact at each end. Although this was a desirable objective, and has since been realized in the instant-start slimline lamps, it was not practically attainable in the early development because of difficulties in manufacture and in finished-lamp performance. The design was therefore changed to provide double contacts at each end of the lamp and the use of starting switches. On problems of that sort, the laboratory, the Standardizing Department, and the factory methods men must cooperate closely.

Other departments of General Electric aided in constructing suitable ballasts and starters. For example, the Transformer Engineering Department at Fort Wayne, Ind., cooperated very helpfully on the ballasts. Westinghouse, as the "A" licensee, also carried on fluorescent-lamp development work, and a useful type of starter known as the glow-switch starter was originated by Westinghouse engineers in the summer of 1938.

INTRODUCING FLUORESCENT LAMPS

In 1935 and 1936 there was still much to be done before fluorescent lamps could be produced in quantity, to say nothing of getting them on the market as a full line. In July, 1935, Lamp Department engineers and research men held a closed meeting at Nela Park with a group of U.S. Navy officers. At that meeting sample fluorescent lamps were displayed and their operating principles explained. The Navy men were the first persons outside the General Electric Co. to see the lamps.

Then in early September of the same year the Illuminating Engineering Society held its annual convention at Cincinnati. General Electric's exhibit booth showed one of the new lamps in operation. The lighting engineers attending were interested but not overwhelmingly impressed. The lamp looked like a highly specialized item. It was 2 feet long and produced a brilliant green light. A display card read, in part: "The fluorescent lumiline lamp—a laboratory development of great promise." This was a real understatement.

More than a year passed. P. J. Pritchard and his colleagues were making progress, but no factory could take on the production job as yet. On Nov. 23, 1936, a dinner in Washington, D.C., celebrating the hundredth anniversary of the founding of the U.S. Patent Office was doubly historic. For the guests were seeing for the first time an application of fluorescent lighting. The new lamps, furnished by General Electric, provided much of the illumination in the large banquet hall.

On April 21, 1938, General Electric announced the introduction of fluorescent lamps as a regular line and they were placed on public sale. A story in *The Magazine of Light* appeared at the same time, stating that "these new light sources provide colored light at efficiencies heretofore unobtainable."

The line of fluorescent tubes first announced included three sizes: 15-watt, 20-watt, and 30-watt, in lengths of 18, 24, and 36 inches respectively. They were offered in seven colors. The list prices ranged from $1.50 to $2.00 according to size.

In the late spring of 1938 the lamps were shown at previews of the New York World's Fair and the Golden Gate Exposition in San Francisco. In the following year millions of visitors to these great shows saw the strange tubular light sources. They were used for several outdoor applications at both world's fairs and for a large interior installation at the New York exposition.

Fluorescent lighting was now officially launched, though of course it was used only on a limited scale in the early months. In October, 1941, the Patent Office granted a patent to George Inman covering the basic principles of practical fluorescent-lamp design. The application for this patent had been filed in April, 1936.

In addition to the Inman patent covering work done in the Lamp Development Laboratory, General Electric had purchased in 1939 the United States rights to a patent application in the names of Meyer, Spanner, and Germer. This patent related to a basic fluorescent-lamp invention made by these three German physicists.

FLUORESCENT-LIGHTING APPLICATIONS

When General Electric first made the lamps available, there were some well-considered differences of opinion in the Lamp Department regarding their future possibilities. This was natural. No one could predict the future of the lamps. They were untried in the field. They were radically different from incandescent bulbs.

Lamp Department managers met in their various committees and considered thoughtfully a long series of questions.

Would customers accept the new tubular shapes, the new patterns of light distribution, and the different color quality of the light from these lamps? Would they accept the comparative bulkiness of the lamps for handling? What about the public's reaction to the base pins and lampholders, quite unlike the conventional screw base and socket of the incandescent bulb? How about the fact that one fluorescent tube could not be replaced in the same fixture or mounting by a lamp of another size?

Would the lamps find their principal use for decoration, to provide attractive colored light? Or would they win part of the general lighting market?

These were hard questions. No one could be positive about the answers. And, as with any new product so markedly different from the old, there were many risks involved in estimating probable volume, manufacturing costs, and sales-promotion budgets.

The businessman wandering wearily home at night doesn't always look puzzled and exhausted just because he has had to dictate a few letters and settle a minor squabble between the file clerks. Sometimes it's because he has been wrestling with perplexing problems that involve not only his own future but the jobs of several hundred or several thousand people as well. Sympathy he doesn't want and perhaps doesn't deserve. But he often does wish he could be certain of all the answers.

At any rate, many people in the Lamp Department—probably the majority—believed in the early months that fluorescent lamps were mainly decorative in purpose. Not many could visualize wide acceptance of the lamps in general lighting applications. True, their efficiency was high, but this was most conspicuous in the production of certain colors—less so in the color qualities desirable for general illumination.

Obviously they were much more expensive to make than incandescent bulbs. They had to sell at higher prices. Purchasers would also have to buy and install auxiliary equipment wherever the lamps were used.

However, the public interest in the lamps was great. A few lamp men felt that there might be a fairly good market for them in general lighting practice. The best thing to do—and the only thing—was to study them thoroughly from the standpoint of application and test them by usage in the field.

The Engineering Division had started to do this before the lamps were placed on general sale. The engineers worked on fixture design and lighting-system design. They figured out how to overcome installation difficulties. All such studies had to be correct and the recommended practice proved by experience if customers were to get satisfactory results. What levels of illumination could be reached with fluorescent lamps in typical applications? What were the problems of brightness, glare, shadows, and cost? The slide rules and the meters were getting a workout in answering these questions. Ward Harrison's vigorous leadership was most notable in solving the many problems.

The outstanding advantages of the lamps, of course, were their modern, streamlined appearance, lower unit brightness, good diffusion, relative coolness, and high efficiency.

Using incandescent bulbs for general lighting, the upper limit of illumination levels is about 50 foot-candles. More light can be provided, but beyond the 50-foot-candle level the radiant heat from the lamps often makes people uncomfortable and becomes a very difficult problem. (This type of heat effect cannot be removed by air conditioning.) Fluorescent lamps have raised the ceiling on foot-candle levels. They provide more light per watt of energy consumed than filament lamps. At the same time, they throw off less radiant heat than incandescent lamps of comparable wattage. Thus the total radiant energy (light plus heat) from a 40-watt white fluorescent lamp is only 9 watts per 1,000 lumens of light; a 200-watt general-service incandescent lamp radiates 43 watts per 1,000 lumens. So the sensation of heat from fluorescent lamps is only about one-fifth that from filament lamps for the same amount of light delivered.

Even with these benefits there was no assurance that fluorescent lighting would take over any appreciable share of the total market. During the year 1938, from April on, the industry sold about 200,000 fluorescent lamps. This was very good, but hardly sensational.

Then, within the next three years, the dam broke so far as the market for these lamps was concerned. In 1939 General Electric introduced a 40-watt 48-inch tube with a high efficiency. Starting at 35 lumens per watt, it was soon rated at 47 lpw because of the improvements made by G-E engineers. This was in the white color designated as 3500° white. By the end of the year the lamp's output had reached 50 lpw. The other sizes were also made available in 3500° white, which many users found preferable to the daylight color quality (6500°) for general lighting.

Fluorescent-lamp sales for the entire industry rocketed to 1.6 million in 1939, to 7.1 million in 1940, and to 21 million in 1941. General Electric engineers, recognizing the public's overwhelming demand for the lamps, worked at a redoubled pace to assure proper usage of the tubes.

The Lamp Department aided any manufacturer of lighting fixtures who wanted to design units that would provide sound, safe, effective lighting.

The Sales and Sales Promotion Divisions stepped up their efforts, too, with advertising and sales activities designed to tell the public the facts about fluorescent lighting.

MORE FLUORESCENT-LAMP DEVELOPMENTS

Soon after the introduction of the 40-watt fluorescent lamp it took the lead in sales, and has been the best seller ever since. General Electric added other sizes, developed new colors in the white and near-white shades, and steadily improved lamp life and efficiency while reducing prices. The 20-watt lamp serves as a good example since it was one of the sizes first introduced. In the first 10 years of making these lamps, G.E. increased the 20-watt tube's efficiency by 44 per cent, boosted lamp life by 150 per cent, and lowered its price by 62½ per cent.

In 1940 and 1941 the Lamp Department built two new plants devoted exclusively to fluorescent-lamp manufacture. These were located at Jackson, Miss., and Bucyrus, Ohio. Each factory was built to accommodate 400 employees and to reach a capacity of about 12 million lamps per year on a three-shift basis. Both plants fabricated glass tubing as well as handling the regular work of lamp assembly. Since that time General Electric has added other fluorescent factories.

The G-E Vapor Lamp Company developed a lamp type known as rectified fluorescent (RF) in 1939. This was a modification of the Cooper-Hewitt lamp with a fluorescent phosphor coating. Used primarily for industrial lighting, it was an excellent lamp for the purpose. It was rated at 85 watts, with 3,000 hours of life and light output of 47 lumens per watt. The tube was 58 inches long and 1¼ inches in diameter. The Vapor Lamp Company manufactured fixtures suited to the lamps. In the same year (1939) the Lamp Department absorbed the Vapor Lamp Company, which ceased to operate as a separate organization. The Lamp Department thus gained some valuable additional personnel. RF fixtures were not sold after 1942 and the lamps were sold only for replacement purposes. The general line of G-E fluorescent lamps took care of most requirements, and the Lamp Department did not want to be in the fixture business.

Early in 1944 General Electric brought out a new line of tubes called "slimline" fluorescent. They were instant-start lamps, long and slim, with single-pin terminals. The line included tubes of ¾-inch and 1-inch diameter at first, and in 1947 was broadened to include lamps 1½ inches in diameter. The lengths in the final complete line were 42, 48, 64, 72, and 96 inches. These tubes have made it possible to emphasize more than ever the "lines of light" appearance in an installation. They are high in efficiency, ranging up to 69 lumens per watt for the standard warm white lamp.

Another interesting development that began in 1943 and appeared on the market in 1945 was the circline lamp. This was a fluorescent tube an inch in diameter bent to the form of a circle 12 inches across and drawing 32 watts. Samples of these lamps were furnished to manufacturers of lighting fixtures and portable lamps so that they could incorporate the tubes in some of their equipment designs. The same practice was followed beginning in

1947 with another size of circline lamps—22 watts, ¾ inch diameter, with the circle measuring 8¼ inches across. In 1952 a third size was added—the 16-inch, 40-watt lamp. Portable-lamp makers have used circline lamps alone, but more often in combination with incandescent bulbs. In that way a generous level of illumination can be obtained, together with pleasing color quality. The lamps are also used for ceiling fixtures, especially in residential lighting, sometimes with two circline sizes in the same fixture.

Fluorescent lamps posed new problems of photometry and testing. Lamp Department technicians built huge photometers and other measuring instruments and devised special test procedures so that this whole class of lamps could be produced and used with the same high quality standards as other General Electric lamps. As with any major new group of products in the lamp field, a new frame of reference had to be established.

GERMICIDAL LAMPS

In 1938 General Electric added germicidal lamps to its lines. Westinghouse had done considerable research to develop this type of lamp prior to 1936. The lamps are generally similar to fluorescent tubes but they do not have phosphor coatings and the special glass tube permits the ultraviolet to come through. They are mercury-vapor lamps producing ultraviolet radiation that is effective in destroying airborne bacteria. Used in hospitals, nurseries, barracks, and classrooms, they are useful in protecting people against infectious diseases. Also, in sterile storage cabinets, meat cases, and similar applications, they aid in the maintenance of healthfulness and cleanliness. They require shielding to avoid damage to the eyes.

General Electric makes germicidal lamps in 8-watt, 15-watt, 30-watt, and 36-watt sizes, plus a 4-watt tube made in a U shape. Since their introduction, Lamp Department engineers have conducted many tests of their effects, worked out additional applications, and improved the lamps.

GLOW LAMPS

Among other electric-discharge sources, neon and argon glow lamps should be mentioned. These are low-wattage lamps made in bulb shapes rather than as tubes. They are not valued for the quantity of light they give, which is low, but for their convenience as signal and pilot lights, night lights, etc., and for their very long life. Their life ratings range from 3,000 to more than 25,000 hours. The sizes run from ⅕₅ watt to 3 watts.

CAPILLARY LAMPS

A fascinating new kind of high-intensity mercury lamp was offered for sale by G.E. in 1938. Known as the capillary lamp, it was first announced in 1936 as a laboratory product created by Dr. Cornelius Bol, a Dutch scientist. General Electric acquired the American rights.

This lamp consists of a small quartz tube about 1½ inches long with an outside diameter of ¼ inch and a bore (interior chamber) only ⅟₁₂ inch across. This diminutive tube contains mercury which vaporizes under very high pressure (more than 1,700 pounds per square inch). This is a *1,000-watt lamp*. This fact, in conjunction with its very small physical dimensions, brings it into the believe-it-or-not class. Producing 65 lumens per watt, it shines like a miniature sun. The brightness seems quite unbelievable.

The lamp as used appears somewhat larger because it must be surrounded by a water-cooling jacket to dissipate the intense heat generated by the tube. There is another type that can be cooled by a rapid stream of air. This was developed by N. T. Gordon and Dr. Whitney of the Schenectady laboratory. Both types, then, require rather complicated auxiliary equipment. Capillary lamps are used for specialized types of searchlights, such as those used at airports for measurement of "ceiling" heights.

Capillary lamps and other unusual types remain unknown to most consumers, but they illustrate the fact that new lighting developments are continually in the making.

"BLACK LIGHT"

Still another application of fluorescence came about with the development of "black light" sources. General Electric started to make these lamps in 1941. They produce ultraviolet radiation that will activate fluorescent materials placed within range of the lamps. There is little visible light from the lamps, so that some interesting and mysterious decorative effects can be achieved on walls, floor coverings, costumes, theater sets, etc. Any design can be created with fluorescent paints or similar substances on the surface to be illuminated. Then the ultraviolet from the lamps causes the design to glow in many hues, yet the observer may be unable to discover the source of the radiation.

Besides their decorative uses, the lamps have several very useful applications—for reading fluorescent signs and maps, for "invisible" laundry and dry-cleaning marks, and so on. G.E. markets four black-light tubes—6-watt, 15-watt, 30-watt, and 40-watt—and a small 4-watt bulb which is designed to operate on low-voltage systems for fluorescent instrument-dial lighting on airplanes.

TYPE RS SUNLAMP

The year 1941 saw the introduction of a new type of G-E sunlamp. The RS sunlamp is a self-contained unit with a 100-watt mercury-discharge element and a 175-watt tungsten-filament resistance ballast. These two major parts are placed in a bulb of the reflector type (with a vaporized-aluminum reflecting surface) which transmits the ultraviolet radiation.

The RS bulb brings great convenience to the use of sunlamps because it fits any regular alternating-current socket and requires no separate auxiliary equipment.

OTHER IMPROVEMENTS

The development specialists and the engineers were busy in the five years immediately preceding World War II making improvements in many of the lamps that had been introduced earlier. Pre-focused flashlight bulbs came along in 1937. Fog lamps for automobiles, using sealed-beam construction, were placed on the market beginning in 1940. New types of infrared heat lamps were added to the line. Sealed-beam and other types of lamps were developed for better illumination in mining operations. There were new kinds of headlights for locomotives. Fluorescent tubes were employed in railroad passenger cars and for other forms of public transportation. In 1940 General Electric offered three-light lamps in the 30–70–100-watt and 50–100–150-watt sizes. These made it possible to design more useful and attractive portable lamps.

As war drew closer, restrictions on the use of materials curbed lighting applications considerably. This was especially true of the rules that had to be established to cover the use of metals for lighting fixtures. New installations were largely confined to industry for several years after 1941. Higher levels of illumination were needed most in the factories where the all-out effort in arms production was under way. Fluorescent lighting, however, was firmly established. It had won tremendous public acceptance. It was to aid on the home front during the years from Pearl Harbor to V-J Day.

CHAPTER 20

Science in the Service of Freedom

As some authorities have pointed out, World War II was an electric war to a great extent. The infantrymen, tank crews, airmen, and sailors had to fight it the hard way and the dangerous way. But at least they were aided and protected as never before by weapons and equipment in which electricity played a vital part. So the General Electric Lamp Department had opportunities to serve in the national war effort.

As in World War I, men and women from the ranks of Lamp Department employees joined the armed services in large numbers —from all the factories, the service districts and sales districts, and from Nela Park. Some gave their lives, others were wounded in battle, all sacrificed many months of normal life to the wartime necessities of their country.

In this, of course, they were no different from millions of other Americans in all walks of life. It is mentioned here only to place in proper perspective the achievements on the home front described in later pages. No matter how many lives were saved by workers at home, the major risks were taken by those in combat. It is with recognition of this fact that the record of the Lamp Department during the war years is written.

In contrast to 1917, the scientific and productive resources of the country were much more ready for mobilization than they had been in the earlier war. To be sure, there were snarl-ups, times of confusion, and duplication of effort in American government and industry. But there was a much stronger realization of American war-production potentialities and better organization to get things rolling. The Lamp Department resources of men and materials, skill and experience, could be put to work quickly on useful projects. Many experts in the department served in uniform in technical capacities. The top scientists in charge of defense research and the Army and Navy leaders had a better idea of their needs than they had had 25 years before. Many of the necessary contacts between them and the Nela Park people had been made before the United States declared war.

LAMPS FOR WARTIME USES

The Lamp Department designed and manufactured more than 300 new types of lamps for wartime use. The Army needed lamps for trucks, tanks, gunsights, signaling, and other uses. The Navy wanted lamps for landing craft, PT boats, submarines, aircraft carriers and airplanes, and every standard type of fighting ship from destroyer escorts to battleships. Calls came in similar variety from the Air Forces, the Coast Guard, the merchant marine, and war industries in a hundred different lines. Anyone would recognize after a moment's thought that it would take a lot of electric lamps to equip a modern military force. But the diversity of the requests had to be experienced at first hand in order to appreciate the importance of lighting and the life-or-death aspects of some of its uses.

There is little that is especially glamorous to tell about these needs and the way they were filled. The particular requirements for a new type of lamp were stated to the researchers and engineers. Then they went to work, utilizing past experience which might or might not have been useful to the lamp business when it occurred. Following their work, the factory men figured out how to make the product in quantity. The foremen, operators, and machines took over. And that was that—another small but essential part of the nation's defense was ready for delivery.

The solutions to these problems were often ingenious and sometimes costly. The process could not always be as smooth as it sounds here. But difficulties, cost, and credit for personal achievement were beside the point. The only consideration was to fill military needs as efficiently and quickly as possible.

Here are some illustrative examples of the lamp developments, though the list is far from complete:

Sealed-beam airplane landing lamps
Airplane recognition lights
Sealed-beam flashing signal lamps
Airplane instrument and indicator lamps—fluorescent, black-light, and incandescent
Sealed-beam lamps for tanks and trucks
Flashtubes—numerous special types
Bomb-target lamps
Special types of high-pressure quartz lamps
Black-light lamps for reading U.S. Navy fluorescent maps
Searchlights for antiaircraft units
Submarine signal and panel lamps
Infrared signaling lamps
Long-life waterproof flashlights for jungle service
Life-jacket and life-raft lamps
Improved running lights for ships

WARTIME ENGINEERING RESEARCH

Whenever and wherever eyes were used in the war there were problems for the Lamp Department to handle. For instance, here is another representative line-up of projects—this time in engineering research:

Blackout lighting problems: streets, motor vehicles, railroads, flashlights, interior lighting, signal lights, sky-glow visibility from sea and air, etc.

Development of antisunburn salve for emergency kits in planes, lifeboats, rubber rafts, etc.

Lighting units for emergency operating rooms aboard ship

Test installations of germicidal lamps in barracks, military hospitals, submarines, laboratories, etc.

Lighting for the inspection of parachutes, cartridge cases, rifle barrels, bullet dies, and dozens of other war-production items

Development of meters and other measuring devices for the armed services

Use of light and glare for camouflage

Research on vision testing, under low-visibility conditions, for night-flying pilots and aerial observers

Use of substitute materials in the design of lighting fixtures

Many such projects cut across departmental lines. The Engineering Division was involved. So were the Lamp Development Laboratory, Standardizing, the Glass Technology Laboratory, and all the factories.

Besides producing new wartime products, the manufacturing experts had to find ways to use substitute materials in order to conserve scarce metals and chemicals. Here are some of the expedients they managed, each of which seems simple in a listing but was not so easy to accomplish:

Steel instead of brass for lamp bases

Use of solder with no tin or low tin content

Substitutes for nickel and copper (for instance, nickel plating instead of solid nickel for lead-in wires, and copper weld wire for pure nickel and copper)

Ethylene glycol for glycerine

Substitutes for rubber

New plating processes

Substitutes for amyl acetate, butyl acetate, and many other chemicals

RADAR AND RADIO-TUBE PROJECT

As was the case at the time of World War I, General Electric scientists in the Schenectady laboratories had developed new types of vacuum tubes. So had their colleagues in the radio and television departments of the company, which were later combined as the Electronics Department. The new tubes were important in radar as well as in radio transmitters and receivers for the armed forces. A notable example was the magnetron tube, an electronic marvel invented by Dr. Albert W. Hull.

In March, 1942, the Schenectady Laboratory asked the Lamp Department to undertake the manufacture of some of these highly intricate tubes. The project was assigned to the Lamp Development Laboratory and the Lamp Facilities Laboratory, where P. J. Pritchard once more took on an arduous series of tasks. Much further development work had to be done, plus the now-familiar activity of translating the laboratory methods into factory accomplishments. So the laboratory men and the Equipment Works staff worked night and day on these demanding assignments.

For example, here are some of the machines and equipment that had to be especially designed and constructed: flange machines, stem machines, beading machines, annealers, grid winding equipment, assembly tables, carbonizing tables, tabulating machines, sealing machines, exhaust equipment, basing machines, and aging racks.

Vacuum-tube manufacture began in 1942. Among the products made by the Lamp Department were thyratrons, cathode-ray tubes, diodes, pentodes, and tubes created for use in walkie-talkie radio sets. Many thousands of tubes, made to the most exacting tolerances, were manufactured for almost three years. Then, at the war's end or shortly before, all vacuum-tube work was turned over to the newly organized G-E Electronics Department.

The experience with electric-discharge light sources helped a great deal in making such tubes as the gas-filled thyratrons. The earlier work with phosphors related to the special phosphor developments for cathode-ray tubes. And the experience of lamp manufacturing generally—working with glass, wire, and other parts—enabled the men and the women on the project to obtain superlative results.

PROXIMITY-FUSE PROJECT

The proximity fuse, a top-secret development during World War II, was in essence a self-powered radio transmitter and receiver with miniature vacuum tubes and other electronic components, small enough to fit into the base of a shell and tough enough to withstand rough handling.

The radio set, marvelously compact, broadcast a continuous wave. When part of the wave was reflected back by a target object, it interfered with the outgoing wave and the shell then exploded at an ideal distance from the target for maximum effect. This high-precision trigger effect was perfectly suited, for instance, to firing at enemy aircraft.

The wonderfully ingenious idea for this device had to be implemented with equally remarkable parts and construction: the vacuum tubes and especially certain small glass ampoules that had to have strength enough to withstand rough handling and yet have great delicacy of response as well.

Progress in developing and producing some of these key parts was slow until the problem was turned over to the Lamp Department. At Nela Park it was apparent to General Electric researchers that the problem was somewhat similar to those encountered in producing various civilian products of the Lamp Department. The parts had to be made with watchlike precision. Nela Park personnel assigned to this project devised the new machinery required. They turned out by the millions the parts necessary for successful use of the proximity fuse. This was done at a cost to the government about one-eighth of the amount that had been paid earlier for less accurate parts from other sources.

The entire project was kept secret. People working on it at Nela Park, Bridgeport, and Schenectady—thousands of General Electric employees—did not know how the end product operated nor the purposes of various parts they were making. The proximity fuse was highly effective in many combat areas—against Japanese kamikaze planes and German buzz bombs, for instance. It aided our forces in the Battle of the Bulge and on Iwo Jima and Okinawa. The proximity-fuse project did not prove by itself that the facilities of American industry were superior to those of our enemies, nor that such facilities were indispensable to the nation's defense. But it was one good indication of these facts.

EMERGENCY SIGNALING MIRROR

The Lamp Department cooperated with the Bureau of Standards in the development and production of an emergency signaling mirror, designed to capture the attention of rescuers. This was for use by fliers forced down at sea or by sailors or any other men adrift in open boats. Wentworth Potter of the Engineering Division was largely responsible for the design of this device so far as the Lamp Department's work on it was concerned. It could not be described as a typical G-E Lamp Department project, but it employed the skill of Lamp Department personnel in a national-defense objective. Therefore it became typical of the wartime efforts of the industry.

To be effective a signaling mirror had to stay bright and perfectly flat under all conditions. It had to be provided with some means for aiming its reflection accurately at a ship on the distant horizon or a plane a few miles away in the sky. As finally produced, the mirror fulfilled these requirements.

It was pocket size. It utilized the process employed in making the reflectors for G-E sealed-beam headlamps. The strong, tempered glass was covered by a film of vaporized aluminum. The coating was capable of sustaining 100 hours of salt-spray test. But perhaps the most intriguing design element was the provision for aiming. There was a cross-shaped aperture at the center of the mirror. This was surrounded by a circle of the exposed rear surface of the aluminum film. The user could sight through the mirror, center the rescuing plane or ship at the middle of the cross-shaped opening, and aim with great accuracy at a "target" miles away. The mirror flashed light from the sun directly toward the rescuers.

Thousands of these signaling mirrors were placed on the lifeboats and rafts carried on ships and airplanes. They helped to save lives. As just one example, there was the situation of a Navy pilot forced down in Tokyo's outer bay. He was found and rescued because he was able to attract the attention of friendly searchers with the mirror.

GUNSIGHT-LAMP PROJECT

The Lamp Department developed gunsight lamps of a special reflector type for aerial warfare. The illumination from these lamps assured better visibility of the target when aiming against a bright background such as a sunlit cloud, desert sand, or haze surrounding the sun.

Coupled with the lamp development was a recording microphotometer. This instrument made it possible to evaluate the performance of experimental lamp designs and to check production. Again, this project was a story growing quite familiar to Lamp Department employees: special machinery, altered methods, precision planning.

WAR-INDUSTRY LIGHTING

During 1941–1945 American industry faced its greatest production tasks. It had to convert from peacetime to wartime production. Many new plants rose where there had formerly been only vacant fields. Modern illumination in old and new factories alike was a "must" if the production goals were to be attained. Good industrial lighting saves working time because workers see faster and more easily; cuts down spoilage and waste of materials; helps prevent costly accidents and injuries; improves employee morale and job satisfaction; helps to keep older, more experienced workmen on the job; promotes better plant housekeeping; and builds better public relations. All these advantages became doubly important in war industry.

Many of the Lamp Department's engineering and sales resources were employed in helping the nation's manufacturers obtain the benefits of good illumination. The General Electric lamp sales force throughout the United States was diverted to the job of removing bottlenecks in lighting, getting 50-foot-candle installations of general illumination into the factories, aiding in the solution of difficult inspection problems, and stepping up efficiency of night-shift operations. General Electric engineers and the lighting specialists of wholesalers, electrical contractors, and the utility companies were enlisted in this effort. From huge shipyards and aircraft plants to the smallest two-man machine shops, these engineers and salesmen created more efficient lighting conditions.

Fluorescent lamps were a big factor in obtaining the needed levels of illumination. Infrared drying lamps saved thousands of hours of time in drying the finishes on war products. Photomicrographic lamps were developed to analyze the grain structure of metals in factory laboratories; they were also used on inspection lines to project magnified images of parts to be inspected. The engineers worked out a variety of techniques for protective lighting to safeguard factories and railroads against sabotage and theft.

The results of this activity were more far-reaching than any statistical estimate could show. The improvements came in "bits and pieces"—five minutes per hour saved on a certain process, 8 per cent less scrap in one department of a factory, and so on. In each case the goods came off the production lines a little faster and a little better-made, simply because workers could see more easily and accurately.

SHOCKPROOF LIGHTING FOR SHIPS

A battleship needs about 20,000 lamps to fill its sockets and carries another 20,000 to 50,000 lamps for use as replacements when necessary. Included in this total are many special types—searchlights, signal lamps, instrument-panel lights, and others. And of course all the Navy's other ships must have lamps, too, in quantities roughly consistent with the size of each ship.

In World War II, where the Navy was more heavily engaged than ever before, the intensive firing of naval guns made necessary even stronger lamps than the usual rough-service type. And the lamps, like everything else aboard, were subject to the terrific shock of hits from enemy torpedoes, guns, bombs, and depth charges. When the Navy reported on these needs, the Lamp Department responded by developing high-impact filament lamps with rubber-cushioned bases.

These were 50-watt bulbs supplying the great majority of a ship's requirements. They gave exceptionally fine service during the war and are still doing so in the Navy's fleets. Among other special applications, the Lamp Department made two-filament lamps for ships' running lights. If one filament failed, the other kept burning until a replacement could be made. This protective feature in naval service is alone enough to justify the development of three-light lamps. It is only one small illustration of how consistent, year-by-year G-E lamp research has benefited our national interests as well as individual well-being.

NOTTINGHAM EQUIPMENT WORKS

A separate division of the Lamp Department was set up in 1942, called the Nottingham Equipment Works, to manufacture highly specialized mechanical devices under a government contract. W. R. Gerow served as manager. This project was related to the intricate firing-control system for aircraft produced by the General Electric Company, with several departments participating.

REGULAR LAMP PRODUCTION

Meanwhile, General Electric maintained its regular and growing production of standard lines of lamps. The manufacture of some types such as Christmas-tree bulbs and other decorative lamps was discontinued for the duration of the war. The materials and the production facilities used for them were regarded as more essential to the special wartime lamps.

By 1945 total shipments of large incandescent lamps by the industry as a whole reached 794 million. Shipments of miniature lamps amounted to 1,131 millions—in other words, well over a billion. The rise in total sales of fluorescent lamps is indicated by the following figures: 1942, 33.6 million; 1943, 37.5 million; 1944, 36.5 million; 1945, 40.7 million. Other major types such as sealed-beam, photoflash, and high-intensity mercury-vapor lamps, were reaching new sales highs in 1945.

MANAGEMENT CHANGES

After 1939 Charles E. Wilson had served as president of General Electric and Philip D. Reed as chairman of the board. Gerard Swope and Owen D. Young retired at the beginning of that year. Wilson, big in stature and big in all-around business ability, had started work as a messenger boy with the Sprague Electric Co., which later became a part of General Electric. From 1899 on he rose steadily in the business, and he moved into the presidency after some years as vice-president in charge of the Specialty Appliance Department. From 1942 to 1944 he served as executive vice-chairman of the War Production Board. At the government's request he took a leave of absence from the presidency of General Electric to assume many of the burdens of keeping America's whole war-production economy in high gear during those critical years.

At Nela Park, M. L. Sloan was appointed general manager of the Lamp Department in 1942. Joseph E. Kewley continued as vice-president in charge until 1945, when Sloan succeeded him. Kewley had guided the business through 11 years of tremendous expansion, including the war-production activities described here. Sloan, an executive who could work out a major policy or follow through on the smallest detail with equal thoroughness, was the logical leader to take over top management of the Department.

When Howard A. Couse retired as manager of the Law Division in 1945, this key position was ably filled by Quincy D. Baldwin. His experience on the company's legal staff in New York and with the General Electric Credit Corporation helped him in meeting the many perplexing legal problems that were facing the lamp business.

There were changes among key personnel in the factories and the sales and service districts from 1940 to 1945—too many, in fact, to be detailed in these pages. The important point is that, as a manager approached the retirement age, there was a planned series of replacements in each organization. Men were continuously being trained for the responsibilities of management. They could move up and maintain without a break the efficient functioning of their units. Age, years of service, being "next in line" through seniority—these were not the primary factors in advancement, though in each case they were considered. So far as it was possible to determine it, proved ability was the principal measuring stick.

At the end of 1945, the Lamp Department payrolls listed nearly 13,000 employees. Competitively, General Electric was in a favorable position in the lamp business. The tasks of reconversion to normal peacetime production could be faced with equanimity on that score. However, as the next chapter explains, the picture was clouded by new legal problems.

CHAPTER 21

Legal Problems

O N JAN. 27, 1941, the Department of Justice brought suit under the antitrust laws against a number of leading companies in the lamp industry. Filed in the U.S. District Court in New Jersey, the suit named General Electric, International General Electric Company, Westinghouse, Hygrade Sylvania, the Consolidated Electric Lamp Co., the Ken-Rad Tube and Lamp Co., the Chicago Miniature Lamp Co., the Tung-Sol Lamp Works, the Corning Glass Works, and several other companies.

For many months before the suit was filed, representatives of the Justice Department searched the files and records of the G-E Lamp Department for information they might use in preparing the case.

The government charged that General Electric had effected a monopoly of the incandescent-lamp industry by means of impermissible agreements with the other defendants in the suit. This was supposed to have begun in or about the year 1927 (the year after the Supreme Court decision in the earlier antitrust case). It is not necessary to detail the charges here, but in essence the government claimed that the General Electric patents, the license agreements, and the distribution system had been used as instruments for controlling the lamp market and reducing competition.

General Electric filed an answer to the complaint on May 15, 1941. The other defendant companies also submitted answers in that year.

Westinghouse, while not admitting to participation in any conspiracy or monopoly, accepted a consent decree on April 10, 1942. By the terms of the decree, Westinghouse agreed to open its existing lamp patents for royalty-free licenses.

Originally set for 1942, the trial was postponed for the duration of the war. The Secretary of War and the Secretary of the Navy requested this postponement since they wanted the facilities, manpower, and management abilities of General Electric to be available for concentration on the war-production effort.

While the war continued and the trial postponement was still in effect, the "B" licenses, with one exception, expired and were not renewed. The licenses of Sylvania, Ken-Rad, Tung-Sol, and Chicago Miniature terminated on Dec. 31, 1944. (Hygrade Sylvania Corporation had changed its name in August, 1942, to Sylvania Electric Products, Inc.)

The "B" license of Consolidated Electric Lamp Co. had been extended in 1939. However, this license was also terminated eventually, so that all "B" licenses were eliminated.

In 1945 another action further changed the previous licensing arrangements. On July 12 General Electric canceled its former "A" license to Westinghouse, effective Aug. 1 of that year.

As the time for the trial neared, another consent decree was entered, this time involving the Corning Glass Works. Under this decree, Corning was ordered to license to all applicants its existing patents relating to lamp glass, without royalties.

TRIAL OF THE ANTITRUST SUIT

Finally, in March, 1946, the trial of the incandescent-lamp antitrust suit began at Trenton, N.J., with Judge Philip Forman presiding.

The hearing of testimony consumed about two months' time. The government brought no witnesses to the stand, but based its case entirely on documents, largely from the files of General Electric and the other companies concerned.

General Electric, on the other hand, while also furnishing plentiful documentary evidence, called a large number of witnesses. These included top executives of the company and of the Lamp Department. The list included Chairman of the Board Philip D.

Reed, President Gerard Swope, Joseph E. Kewley, M. L. Sloan, F. F. Harroff, and Dr. Zay Jeffries. Executives of several licensee companies also testified, including men from Sylvania, Consolidated, Tung-Sol, and Chicago Miniature.

Judge Forman handed down his opinion on Jan. 19, 1949. He found that General Electric had violated the antitrust laws in certain respects. The final judgment to implement this opinion was entered on Oct. 8, 1953.

JUDGMENT IN THE INCANDESCENT-LAMP SUIT

One thing the government asked for in this case was the divestiture of one-half of General Electric's lamp-production facilities. A complete description of this request would be quite complicated, but essentially this is what the government was asking:

That the lampmaking and parts-making facilities of the G-E Lamp Division be divided into equal halves, as measured by productive capacity; and that one-half be put up for sale under the jurisdiction of the court.

The practical problems of making an equal division of the business would obviously be incredibly difficult. But the main point for the court to decide was whether divestiture was necessary or desirable.

After considerable discussion of this question, the judge's opinion in connection with the decree stated that: "In sum, divestiture of General Electric is neither feasible nor in the public interest. As divestiture of General Electric is not necessary to foster competition, the Government's request therefor will be denied."

Another major request by the government was that the General Electric Company should be enjoined from using the agency system of lamp distribution. Here again the court denied the request, pointing out that the agency system had been found valid by the Supreme Court in the 1926 case.

On these two important points, then, Judge Forman ruled against the government. However, on a number of other questions the court decreed changes in the conduct of General Electric's lamp business.

Not only G.E. but all the defendant companies were ordered to dedicate to the public all existing patents on lamps and lamp parts. This meant that all such patents in effect or applied for at the time of the judgment could be freely used by anyone—they were placed in the public domain.

All the companies involved were also directed to make available licenses at reasonable royalty rates on their existing patents for lampmaking machinery.

General Electric was also required to license (at reasonable royalty rates) its *future* patents on lamps, lamp parts, or machinery. This applied to patents owned by the company within five years after the date of the judgment.

General Electric was further directed to supply certain technical information about the processes and methods used in connection with the various patents. This information would be supplied on request to anyone entitled to use the patents, provided the request was made within three years of the date of the judgment.

These were the most significant points. There were also a considerable number of additional injunctions placed on General Electric and the other companies. Many of these referred to practices which G.E. had voluntarily ceased when their legality had been questioned by the government some years before.

FLUORESCENT-LAMP ANTITRUST SUIT

On Dec. 9, 1942, the Department of Justice filed a separate complaint in regard to the fluorescent-lamp business. Like the other antitrust suit, the case was postponed for the duration of the war. The charges were similar in most respects to those in the incandescent-lamp suit.

General Electric began negotiations with the government in November, 1953, to arrive at a settlement of the fluorescent-lamp case. On March 26, 1954, the company accepted a consent decree. Its major provision was that General Electric would give royalty-free licenses on all its fluorescent-lamp patents held or applied for prior to the date of the decree.

PART FIVE

Light for a Bright Future

CHAPTER 22

Postwar Progress

IT DID NOT take long for the Lamp Department management and the employees in every division to resume normal activities after the war. Postwar planning had been an integral part of management thinking and action for many months before the final victory was won.

New factories had been planned for the resumption of peacetime business. Studies had been made of probable demand for major lines of lamps. The engineers had prepared for a complete revamping of the Lighting Institute. These blueprints for the future typified the advance thinking throughout the business.

THE NEW-PRODUCT PARADE CONTINUES

Almost at once the inventive skills of the development engineers brought forth additional products. Within a year after the Japanese surrender they had created more than 20 new lamps and brought them into production. Among them were the following: airplane and train reading lamps using reflector bulbs, ready to brighten the streamlined transportation equipment then being built; several new infrared lamps; an improved sealed-beam automobile headlamp, with an increase of 5 watts to get a more powerful beam. In the miniature-lamp field, there were improved Christmas-tree lamps and even a novel smoke-producing lamp for toy trains.

Routine machine development had been suspended during the

war. Now the mechanical specialists could go ahead, free of restrictions. And go ahead they did. Descriptions of their accomplishments are necessarily so technical that detailing the new devices they produced annually after 1945 would be more confusing than enlightening here. As one example, however, they created an improved machine that applied the liquid phosphor coating to fluorescent lamps and then dried the lamps. It handled this critical process at the unprecedented rate of 3,500 tubes per hour. In 1947 the equipment experts took in stride the assignment of building a complete new line of machinery for making slimline lamps.

The flow of new lamps increased in the five years from 1947 to 1952. The reflector spot and flood line gained a 75-watt R-30 bulb. New fluorescent and photoflash lamps came from the laboratories.

The light output of G-E fluorescent lamps moved upward 17 per cent over-all from 1945 to 1952; also, their rated lives were greatly lengthened during this period. The public was getting more light for its money. The gains in efficiency were achieved largely by development of new phosphors and coating methods. A new high for light output from a fluorescent lamp in the white or near-white colors was established with the 96-inch slimline lamp: 69 lumens per watt. G.E. brought out de luxe cool-white and de luxe warm-white fluorescent tubes, both of which produced flattering color effects for people's complexions, for foods, and for fabrics.

PAR bulbs (sealed-beam type) were especially designed for locomotive headlights and for floodlights. A complete new line of ceramic-coated, colored incandescent lamps provided brighter colors and more efficient light production.

Also during these years Marvin Pipkin devised a new inside coating for incandescent lamps—the Q coat. This is a coating of smoke-thin particles of silica. It diffuses the light so well that there are no areas of intense brightness in contrast to the remainder of the bulb. After Pipkin's original work, development proceeded under the direction of D. E. Elmendorf, with another group of engineers working out applications.

G.E. first used the Q coat for the 150-watt white indirect-lite bulb for portable-lamp use.

General Electric also introduced Q-coat bulbs in the standard household sizes—first in the 100-watt and then in the 60-watt size. Three-light bulbs also had the Q coat. As a result, the light was uniformly diffused—softer, less glaring.

One of the typical problems in the average home is the "shower type" of ceiling fixture. These units have sockets that hold two, three, or five bulbs burning base-up. The bulbs are almost always unshaded and make an annoying source of glare, with rather spotty distribution of light. Early in 1950 General Electric introduced the 50-GA bulb, a new type especially designed to modernize these fixtures and make them much more useful.

The wartime experience of having to substitute steel for brass in incandescent lamp bases had its effect on lampmaking after the war. General Electric metallurgists and base-manufacturing specialists went one step further and produced satisfactory aluminum bases. Most standard lamp bases are now made of aluminum. The same light, bright metal was adopted in sturdy bases for fluorescent tubes.

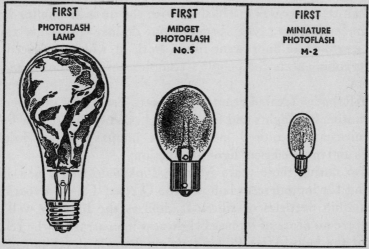

FIRST PHOTOFLASH LAMP — FIRST MIDGET PHOTOFLASH No.5 — FIRST MINIATURE PHOTOFLASH M-2

Photoflash lamps have been reduced in size, making them easier to use, more convenient to carry and store. The new M2 bulb not only costs less but also permits the use of smaller equipment.

In 1954 General Electric announced a remarkably compact new photoflash bulb, known as the M2. This tiny bulb gave a high-intensity flash of light, suitable for many needs of amateur and professional photographers, yet it was so small that it could be carried and used in quantity very easily. It also permitted the development and use of smaller reflectors without loss of quality in flash photography.

CHAPTER 23

Seventy-five Years of Progress

LIGHT's DIAMOND JUBILEE, celebrated in 1954, found the lamp industry so far advanced, so thoroughly integrated into American habits of life, that the pioneers of lamps and lighting would have been amazed to see it, no matter how grandiose their hopes and dreams had been.

In the G-E Lamp business, development and quality control of manufacturing had reached heights of precision never before known. More than 40 factories produced not only finished lamps, large, miniature, and all other types, but all integral parts as well —glass, wire, bases, chemical products, and all other components. Manufacturing, engineering, and marketing, and the general staff services of law, finance, and employee relations were all blended into the over-all picture of modern business action. The somewhat more routine functions, such as purchasing, accounting, and plant maintenance, also played their parts in making the business successful.

MANAGEMENT PROGRESSION

In 1950 the General Electric Company selected a new president: Ralph J. Cordiner. After long experience in the company's appliance business at Bridgeport, Conn., he had been elected a vice-president in 1945 and executive vice-president in 1949. Upon the retirement of Charles E. Wilson late in 1950, Mr. Cordiner was elected to the top executive position. His unique knowledge of business organization, his keen marketing sense, and his confidence in the future of the electrical industry played a major role in the rapid postwar expansion of the company.

In the Lamp Department, Fred F. Harroff was named general manager in 1948. When Martin L. Sloan retired in 1950, Harroff became the new vice-president. He joined the company in 1920, working for 10 years in the Sales Department and then transferring to the Administration staff. Before his appointment as assistant general manager in 1943, his analyses of the operations of the business materially aided the preceding vice-presidents in forming policy.

Upon Harroff's retirement in 1953, a new vice-president for G-E lamps was named, Donald L. Millham, who had served as comptroller of General Electric since 1946. Millham's long experience in auditing and tax accounting for the company, beginning in 1927, made him familiar with the financial problems that are so vital in today's business management. His administrative staff included Ralph H. Humbert as manager of marketing, Carl L. Olson as manager of engineering, and Kenneth G. Reider as manager of manufacturing.

Consistent with new company nomenclature, the name of the Lamp Department was changed to the Lamp Division of General Electric.

THE DYNAMICS OF RESEARCH IN SEEING

In the early days of lampmaking, one of the greatest aims was to maintain a strong engineering department. Such a department included many functions that are now allocated to other groups in the greatly expanded operations of today's lamp business. Yet a description of some of the work done currently by the G-E lamp engineers typifies, perhaps, the continuing spirit of research that animates the business.

The daily activities of the Application Engineering Department often bear directly on market development. At the same time, the engineers are constantly trying to find the answers to many complicated questions about lamps, about lighting, about *seeing*. It seems likely that the engineers gained as much additional knowledge in the first few years after World War II as in any comparable period.

Ward Harrison remained as manager of the department until 1949, when he retired from the company but continued his active career as a consulting engineer. The new manager was Willard C. Brown, whose connection with the department began in 1920.

The organizational chart of the Application Engineering Department shows several basic fields of research. It also indicates a series of specific lighting fields, with specialists assigned to each. Without following the language of the organization chart, the listing below is merely a sampling of the types of research carried on in this department:

Research in the physiology and functioning of the eyes, and other studies in the Science of Seeing

Research in brightness and glare—for example, the establishment of glare ratings for lighting installations

Research in color—such as studies of the color effects of various light sources in specific installations

Research in lighting-system design and the economics of light production

Research in radiant energy—such as measuring and studying the effects of radiation from germicidal lamps and sunlamps

Research in the measurement of light—studying lamps and equipment photometrically, developing new measuring instruments, etc.

Research in specific lighting applications—working on lamp design; working with the manufacturers of lighting equipment in a dozen or more fields.

Obviously these listings overlap. They are incomplete. But they give some indication of the scope of the department's work. These engineers are concerned with farm lighting, home lighting, store lighting, sports and floodlighting, the illumination of offices, churches, industrial plants, mines, railroads, service stations, automobiles, and the lighting for photography, moving pictures, television, aviation, and so on ad infinitum.

In addition, there is a section devoted to engineering publications covering every conceivable lighting application, from the theater to the dentist's chair, from deep-sea diving to the development of healthy livestock.

Until recently the Lighting Institute was an activity supervised by the Engineering Department. In 1946 the Institute was closed for several months to permit a complete interior reconstruction. Every square foot was remodeled with a view toward presenting lamp and lighting information in new ways, taking advantage of new techniques in display and instructional method. This had been planned on the drawing boards all through 1945. The rebuilt Institute was beautifully designed in modern style. In February, 1951, it became a separate department in the Marketing Group, with Henry J. Chanon as manager. A year later Chanon returned to the Sales Department and James C. Forbes was appointed manager of the Lighting Institute.

SALES AND SERVICE

In 1947 the Eastern and Western sales-division arrangement was discontinued. Two years earlier Edwin E. Potter, who had managed Eastern Sales, advanced to a General Electric vice-presidency and left the Lamp Department. Also in 1947, N. H. Boynton transferred from Western Sales to become a consultant on the Administration staff. The new general sales manager was Philip D. Parker.

During the last 20 to 30 years distribution of lamps has broadened to include wholesalers and retailers in the grocery, drug, and similar lines of business, as well as the electrical and hardware fields. This has been a convenience to users. The agency plan, with its long record of successful operation, continues as before for G-E lamps, with a few minor changes.

If the G-E lamp salesman, battling against the forces of depression, enabled the Lamp Department to hold its own in 1932 and similar years, it is no less true today that the salesman's work is the ultimate factor in maintaining jobs, security, and profit for the business.

As of the time this is written, the Lamp Division operates 35 district sales offices. Each is a small business in itself, run by a responsible manager. These managers make the business tick by combining the salesman's enterprise with the leavening wisdom of management experience.

G-E lamp advertising goes forward as usual, telling the public not only about lamps but also about all the benefits of better illumination in a dozen or more fields. It is solidly backed by a separate market research department, by engineering research, and by the development and manufacturing facilities described previously. For example, the advertising claims would mean little unless the factory operators, supervisors, and managers did their job well.

Light Magazine continues to hew to the established line of high editorial standards. (Lawrence W. O'Brien served as editor for six years, beginning in 1946, and was succeeded by Arthur E. Earley.)

Finally, the Lamp Division has 19 service districts, each with its main warehouse and, in some instances, subsidiary warehouses. Shipments of any size by rail, truck, water, or air transportation are all part of the day's routine to the men and women serving these district offices.

CHAPTER 24

"A Business Is People"

A LEADING INDUSTRIALIST recently pointed out that "a business is people." The buildings, machinery, and raw materials are essential. There would be no jobs and no production without the capital investment of those willing to take financial risks. But to a large extent, a business *is* people. The General Electric Company recognizes that fact. For many years it has operated accordingly in its treatment of employees in all capacities.

The record of pay increases and tangible employee benefits over many years compares favorably with that of any industry with similar product costs and price conditions. Other benefits include overtime pay, a bonus for night-shift work, paid vacations, and pay for holidays.

SECURITY PROGRAM

General Electric safeguards the health and safety of its workers with every available medical and protective means. The larger factories maintain well-equipped dispensaries, with doctors and nurses on duty. The company gives all new employees physical examinations to be sure they are fit and to protect their health in case of any ailment requiring treatment.

The employee insurance plan, in effect since 1939, provides for weekly payments in case of any illness that keeps a worker from his job longer than a week. It includes a full schedule of hospitalization benefits and surgeon's fees. Hospital, surgical, and maternity benefits for the employee's dependents are available, too. The life-insurance coverage amounts to about 1½ times normal annual earnings.

The General Electric pension plan is designed to provide retirement income for employees at all levels. About two-thirds of the cost of the pension plan is paid by the company and one-third by the employee. The same proportions apply to the insurance plan.

General Electric encourages its employees to become stockholders in their company. Those who buy U.S. Savings Bonds by payroll deduction and leave them in the custody of the company for five years receive a bonus of General Electric common stock equal to 15 per cent of the purchase price of the bonds.

For years the company has maintained an employee-relations activity, implementing the security program and providing recreational facilities, training opportunities, etc.

In 1945 a new industrial relations program was started at Nela Park. This has grown to be the Employee and Plant Community Relations Department. Its staff aids the factories and other departments with a full program in this important field. Their work embraces community relations in each town or city where a G-E lamp plant is located. Its purpose is to enhance the safety, health, and security of more than 17,000 Lamp Division employees; to make their working places pleasant; and to help make their communities good places for them and their families to live. This department, with its counterpart in each G-E lamp plant, underlines the belief that "a business is people."

THE LAMP OF RESEARCH

Edison's original lamp, which burned for about 40 hours, marked the beginning of all that we know today as the modern electrical industry.

The successors of that feebly glowing bulb have lighted ever more brightly the lives of countless people. As the Coolidges, the Langmuirs, and the other creators in the art of lighting have made their contributions, each generation has been able to live a richer life.

The G-E lamp business has grown and prospered only through the ability of its men and women to keep progressing steadily toward the same objective—better lighting for more people at the lowest possible cost.

Today the users of General Electric incandescent lamps are getting more than 25 times as much light for each lamp dollar as from the first tungsten lamps introduced in 1907. The average list price of General Electric lamps, taking them all together, is lower than in 1939—this despite the effects of inflation, with its higher costs of materials, manpower, and taxes. Small increases in price on some types and sizes have had to be made since 1945, but in general prices are below prewar levels.

Gains like these in lamp and lighting value have been possible because General Electric believes in continuing research in every department of its business.

There are mistakes and errors of judgment in the lamp business as in every human activity. The average of accomplishment, however, is high. The level of integrity is high.

Whenever the horizon of lamp and lighting research seems to be coming closer, someone predicts that all the important discoveries have been made, and that no others will occur. Almost as soon as the words leave his lips, a new and better light source or lighting method is announced.

The men and women in the General Electric lamp business are determined that the light of research shall never go out.

Index